SpringerBriefs in Pharmaceutical Science & Drug Development

For further volumes:
http://www.springer.com/series/10224

Daria Mochly-Rosen • Kevin Grimes
Editors

A Practical Guide to Drug Development in Academia

The SPARK Approach

Editors
Daria Mochly-Rosen
Kevin Grimes
Department of Chemical and Systems Biology
Stanford University School of Medicine
Stanford, California
USA

ISSN 1864-8118 ISSN 1864-8126 (electronic)
ISBN 978-3-319-02200-0 ISBN 978-3-319-02201-7 (eBook)
DOI 10.1007/978-3-319-02201-7
Springer Cham Heidelberg New York Dordrecht London

Library of Congress Control Number: 2013951226

Printed on acid-free paper

Springer is part of Springer Science+Business Media (www.springer.com)

We dedicate this book to our SPARKees–Stanford faculty, postgraduate fellows, and students who have stepped beyond the confines of traditional academia to embrace the challenges of drug discovery and development. We are inspired by your efforts to translate your discoveries into new treatments that will benefit patients, and we have learned a great deal from each of you.

Preface

Our intention in putting together this volume, *A Practical Guide to Drug Development in Academia: The SPARK Approach*, was not to generate a comprehensive "how to" book; this topic cannot be taught in 150 pages. Rather, this volume is an answer to requests from our own SPARKees as well as from other academic institutions that have established or are planning to establish their own translational research programs. This book provides 4–5 pages on each topic that is part of the long process of drug development. The book is intended for novices who embark on this amazing path of translating basic research or clinical findings into new therapeutics to benefit patients. Ideally, you will read this book before you begin this translational effort, so that you will understand the path ahead, start planning what the final product will be ("target product profile" in the industry lingo), and then create a path back to where the project is today–doing it the industry way, with our own academic twist. This book should also be useful for students and postdoctoral fellows who plan a career in industry or who hope that their academic career will be translational in nature.

SPARK at Stanford is now in its seventh year. The program evolved slowly. We have found a certain formula that works well for our academician inventors and we hope that it will work for all. This book was written mainly by our SPARK mentors–the true engine for the success of the program. It is not a complete guide to what needs to be done but provides a general overview of the important topics in the development process.

Drug development is applied science with a concrete goal in mind. A successful program will require contributions from experts in multiple disciplines (chemistry, biology, pharmacology, toxicology, medicine, regulatory science, statistics, and many more). Since no single person can master all of these disciplines, we encourage you to seek advice liberally from experts in the field. By peppering the various chapters with lessons that surprised me since my initiation into biotechnology entrepreneurship 12 years ago, I hope to demonstrate how, at least for me, drug development is not necessarily intuitive. You will find these in boxed text throughout the chapters.

After working on my own translational research projects and now mentoring over 70 other academic projects, I can summarize the following key lessons that I have learned.

1. Check your ego at the door–drug discovery is not about any one person; it is a true team effort, requiring experts in multiple disciplines. The weakest link is standing between you and total failure.
2. Consult, consult, consult–there is always someone who knows much more than you about what is needed (preferably more than one person). Find these individuals and get their advice.
3. Always continue to apply your own judgment, as even experienced advisors can be wrong.

As the editors of this volume, Kevin Grimes and I hope that you will find it useful in your endeavor.

And now–Let's SPARK

Stanford, CA, USA Daria Mochly-Rosen

Acknowledgements

We wish to express our sincere gratitude to Dr. Emily Egeler for her tireless efforts to bring this volume to completion. Thanks also to our many contributing authors, who have generously shared their expertise and knowledge to help advance the cause of academic drug discovery. Special thanks to Dr. Phil Pizzo, the previous Dean of Stanford University School of Medicine, who endorsed the SPARK program from the start, and to our current Dean, Dr. Lloyd Minor, for his continued and unwavering support. Lastly, we owe a tremendous debt of gratitude to our SPARK advisors, whose generous and loyal support has been instrumental in SPARK's success.

–DM-R & KVG

Contents

Chapter 1
Getting Started

Daria Mochly-Rosen and Kevin Grimes

In recent decades, we in academia have focused on advancing scientific understanding through basic research and counted on the biopharmaceutical industry to translate promising discoveries into new therapeutics. Given the recent developments, however, this paradigm needs to change. Pharmaceutical companies have drastically cut their research budgets and basic research staffs to decrease costs and improve short-term profits. Additionally, the number of biotechnology venture funds has contracted, especially those that invest in new biotechnology start-up companies. As a result, we can expect that fewer novel drug programs will originate in the biopharmaceutical sector. Academic inventors can and should step in to fill this gap in the discovery pipelines. But we often lack the expertise and resources to advance our projects through this applied science stage of drug discovery and development. This chapter introduces the process of drug development and highlights some of the important first steps: understanding the clinical needs, developing a target product profile (which defines the new drug's essential characteristics), and adopting a project management approach. These essential steps not only increase the likelihood of success, but can also help decrease both the cost and time required to accomplish our goal. Translating discoveries from bench to bedside is a challenging, but incredibly rewarding process, allowing us to advance scientific discovery and ensure that our government-funded research translates into improved health for our society.

D. Mochly-Rosen (✉)
Chemical and Systems Biology, Stanford University School of Medicine, 269 Campus Drive, Center for Clinical Science Research Rm 3145a, Stanford, CA 94305-5174, USA
e-mail: sparkmed@stanford.edu

K. Grimes
Chemical and Systems Biology, Stanford University School of Medicine, 269 Campus Drive, Center for Clinical Science Research Rm 3145c, Stanford, CA 94305-5174, USA
e-mail: kgrimes@stanford.edu

D. Mochly-Rosen and K. Grimes (eds.), *A Practical Guide to Drug Development in Academia*, SpringerBriefs in Pharmaceutical Science & Drug Development,
DOI 10.1007/978-3-319-02201-7_1,

1.1 Advancing New Treatments to the Clinic Within Academia

Daria Mochly-Rosen

In 2000, our laboratory demonstrated that a rationally designed inhibitor of the delta isozyme of protein kinase C (δPKC) reduced infarct size after heart attack by 70% in a rat model. The basic research that led to this result began more than a decade earlier. Our laboratory had studied protein–protein interactions and their specific role in PKC-mediated signal transduction. Because we needed tools to probe these protein–protein interactions, we discovered a methodology to design selective peptide inhibitors and activators of the individual members of the PKC family of enzymes (isozymes). After confirming the effect of these modulators *in vitro*, we replicated these effects in cultured cells.

How did our lab begin studying heart attack? In 1997, I presented our data at the American Heart Association Meeting. Using the peptide regulators of protein–protein interactions, we found that two PKC isozymes activated by adrenaline in the heart caused opposite effects: one increased and the other decreased the rate of contraction of cardiac muscle cells in culture. I thought that regulating contraction rate of the heart would interest cardiologists. To my dismay, my report triggered no response whatsoever.

Box 1.1: Key Terms and Abbreviations

PKC: protein kinase C
Isozyme: family of closely related enzymes that catalyze similar reactions
OTL: Office of Technology Licensing; the university group responsible for managing intellectual property
IND: Investigational New Drug application; document filed with the FDA prior to initiating research on human subjects using any drug that has not been previously approved for the proposed clinical indication, dosing regimen, or patient population
FDA: US Food and Drug Administration
Repurposed drug: an FDA-approved drug with a new indication, formulation or route of administration

Dr. Joel Karliner, the Chief of Cardiology at the University of California at San Francisco, was kind enough to point out the problem. He stopped me as I was leaving the lecture hall and told me that regulation of contraction rate is of limited clinical importance. He advised, "Focus instead on determining the role of PKC in heart attack." He also suggested that I take a cardiology fellow into my laboratory "just to keep us informed." I invited Mary Gray, M.D., to join my group as we set out to examine the potential clinical uses for our basic research tools. In less than three years, we had shown that we could substantially reduce the infarct size of heart attacks *in vivo* by treating animals with the δPKC inhibitor. Surely, the pharmaceutical industry would now be pounding on our doors!

Box 1.2: Recommendation

Having a clinician as part of a basic research team can provide a real advantage when considering translational opportunities. When a basic discovery is made, the team has an opportunity to consider whether it also has clinical relevance. Understanding a clinical need is not necessarily intuitive; why not engage clinicians early to help identify how our discoveries may be put to clinical use? *–DM-R*

With the help of the Office of Technology Licensing (OTL), we secured our intellectual property through patent filings. To our surprise, the pharmaceutical companies were not remotely interested in our findings. We heard an assortment of reasons: "Rats are easy to cure"; "Peptides are not drugs"; "Kinases are poor drug targets." Out of complete frustration that a potentially life-saving treatment garnered absolutely no interest from the industry, I founded KAI Pharmaceuticals together with my student, Dr. Leon Chen. We visited scores of venture groups over 18 months attempting to raise funding for KAI. Finally, after a successful pre-IND meeting with the Food and Drug Administration (FDA) in 2003 with our clinical advisor, Dr. Kevin Grimes, and a handful of other consultants, we convinced investors to fund us. In 2004, I took a leave of absence from Stanford to serve as the chief scientific officer of the company for its first year.

1.1.1 SPARKing Translational Research in Academia

During my year at KAI, I became interested in creating a program that would help drug and diagnostic development in academia. It was clear to me that there were many clinically valuable discoveries at Stanford's OTL that were not licensed. These inventions may be considered less attractive for many reasons including: (1) lack of proof-of-concept data in animals; (2) poorly characterized new chemical entity or drug that the industry has no or little experience with (e.g., our peptide inhibitors); (3) addresses a clinical indication that is known to be difficult (e.g., expensive clinical trials, like Alzheimer's disease and/or indications where pharma had prior failures, such as stroke); or (4) a therapeutic target (e.g., a particular receptor) without a drug that modifies its activity. Even something as promising as an entirely new therapeutic platform is now considered unattractive (although these were preferred in the 1990s) because of the long development time.

In other words, academic inventions are generally deemed to be premature and therefore too risky for pharma and/or investors. I believe that academic institutions must develop these discoveries further within academia if they are to attract commercial interest. We can also advance some of our discoveries directly to the clinic without commercial support, particularly when developing diagnostics or "repurposed" drugs. It is our social responsibility to step into this gap so that our discoveries will benefit patients.

1.1.2 What is SPARK?

SPARK is a hands-on training program in translational research that I founded in 2006 and now co-direct with Dr. Kevin Grimes. Each cycle of training lasts 2 years and we are now in our seventh cycle.

SPARK's mission is to accelerate the transition of basic discoveries in biomedical science to FDA-approved drugs and diagnostics. SPARK provides training opportunities in translational research to faculty members, postdoctoral fellows and students. Our goals are to move five to ten new discoveries each year from the lab to the clinic and/or to commercial drug and diagnostic development.

Each autumn, we select approximately 15 new projects to participate in SPARK. We first assemble a selection committee of representatives from Stanford and the local biotechnology community. OTL provides us with disclosures of unlicensed discoveries from the prior year that may be developed into drugs, biologics, or diagnostics. We also solicit proposals from across the university. SPARK selection criteria are quite simple:

1. The invention addresses an important unmet clinical need
2. The approach is novel
3. Two years of SPARK support will increase the likelihood that the invention will enter clinical trials and/or be licensed

Finalists are invited to compete for funding from the program. (Although access to the funding is limited to ~15 new projects each year, any university member can attend the meetings and obtain advice.) When preparing their presentation, the inventors follow a SPARK template that requires information beyond the background science. After presenting a scientific introduction, presenters focus on the clinical benefits and basic requirements of their product (Target Product Profile, discussed in Sect. 1.4) and propose a development plan with specific funding requests and milestones. In other words, the inventor is asked to plan from the product back to the experiments that will generate it. We encourage this project management mindset—a thinking process that is more prevalent among industry scientists than academic researchers—because novel discoveries can only advance towards a clinical therapeutic by following a disciplined path of applied science during development.

Importantly, unlike regular seed grants that go directly to the lab's account, SPARK funding (averaging ~$50,000/year for 2 years) is managed centrally and is paid only for pre-agreed upon milestones; money that has not been used in time reverts to the general fund pool and may end up supporting another SPARK project.

Experts from local biotechnology and pharmaceutical companies join our inventors each Wednesday evening. The success of SPARK is dependent on these experts who volunteer their time and who agree not only to complete confidentiality, but also to assign any inventions resulting from their advising activity at SPARK to our university.

1.1.3 I Love Wednesdays

This is a comment that we often hear as people are reluctantly leaving the room at the end of our SPARK sessions. Between 80 and 100 people join us every Wednesday night throughout the year in a room that is bustling with energy and excitement. During the two hour meeting, SPARK inventors (aka SPARKees) either present progress reports on their project or listen to an interactive lecture by an industry expert on a topic related to drug or diagnostics discovery and development. (The book that you are holding introduces briefly the topics of these lectures.) Each inventor presents a progress report every 3 months or so, and the amount of progress often surprises even the most experienced SPARK advisors. The benefit of the meetings comes from the strong commitment of the advisors to share their knowledge and experience in real-time. This feedback is invaluable in helping the SPARKees to overcome challenges and find a path forward to achieving their goals.

1.1.4 SPARK Track Record of Success

SPARK is in its 7th year of existence. The educational value of the program is substantial for graduate students, postdoctoral fellows and faculty. The experience is particularly helpful for trainees who are seeking positions in industry. However, a more quantitative measure of SPARK's success can be assessed by four parameters:

1. Licensing of projects (to a funded company)
2. Entry into clinical trials
3. Publications
4. Research funding awarded to SPARKees that they attributed to the work they carried out in SPARK

As of summer 2013, a total of 32 projects have completed their participation in SPARK. Of these, 19 were either licensed and/or moved into the clinic; a *success rate exceeding* 50%! We also collected information on grants enabled by SPARK participation. To our surprise, based on participants' reports, the return was about $5 for every $1 invested by the school. Although SPARK is a relatively young program, we are on track to maintain a similar success rate in the future. As SPARK establishes a history of valuable projects, we are seeing more industry interest in collaborating or licensing—even for our early discovery-stage projects.

Box 1.3: Recommendation

Translational research is complementary to basic research, but should not be conducted at the expense of basic research. Medical schools will weaken themselves if the pendulum swings too far in favor of translational research. *–DM-R*

What is lacking in this analysis is the economic impact of new product sales on the academic institution. This is not an accidental omission; the impact can be measured only many years later. It takes 10–15 years for commercialization of a new drug. If academic institutions invest in translational research hoping for revenues, there is a risk that their programs will become risk-averse, focusing on low-hanging fruit with limited impact on patient care, or on indications that have large markets (e.g., another anti-erectile dysfunction drug) rather than a true novel therapeutic for an unmet clinical need. If SPARK is rewarded for innovation, for getting programs to the clinic regardless of the commercial value, and for impact on the drug and diagnostic development process in general, we may be able together to have a true impact on patients' health and health care costs.

1.1.5 Should Academia be Engaged in Advancing Early Inventions?

You might believe the answer is obvious. However, during my many years of discussions with colleagues, I have learned that perhaps not all arguments in favor of translational research efforts in academia are apparent. Here are some that I find compelling.

- It is our social responsibility: Most of our research is supported by public funds and therefore we should make an effort, if our work can be translated to novel therapeutics or diagnostics, to make it attractive and useful for development by industry.
- It fits our education mission: The majority of our graduates who do not land academic positions are likely to work in industry. It is therefore an opportunity to educate them on the development process and through them, educate the industry on what academia's contribution can be.
- It is pure fun: Academicians often hold the opinion that industry's work is applied science, and therefore less intellectually demanding or gratifying. My 1 year in industry and the years that followed taught me that this is an incorrect notion. The work of drug and diagnostic development is intellectually challenging and a really exciting and worthwhile activity.
- It is an opportunity: The success rate of drug discovery and development is still dismal and the consequences of failures greatly impact our health care costs. There is a special role and advantage for academicians in improving public health through drug and diagnostic development. First is the cultural difference

between industry and academia. While industry by nature is risk averse, academia gives higher rewards to risk takers—innovation and impact on the field are key components in faculty promotion and awards. In addition, academics are not burdened by knowledge of what can fail and has failed in industry; there is little published work on the topic, so we are free to apply new ideas to old problems. Further, academia can rely on the enthusiasm and brilliance of our students who are the major engines of our research and innovation. Finally, there is a disincentive in industry to share information. On the other hand, in academia, all that we learn is passed on through teaching and publications and thus can positively impact industry, which can translate into better health and lower health care costs.

Box 1.4: What Surprised an Academician?

Good science is important for raising funds from venture capitalists. But equally important are a clear and logical plan to develop a product, a strong team to run the company, and a positive attitude. We can't allow our egos to stand in the way. Rejection rates in drug development for funding or licensing are even higher than those for paper submissions or grant applications. *–DM-R*

Without a doubt, basic research is essential for our mission and should remain the main focus of academic research. However, I strongly believe that it is our responsibility as academic institutions to contribute to the development of leads for drugs and diagnostics to benefit society.

Box 1.5: The Bottom Line

SPARK's mission is to accelerate the transition of basic discoveries in biomedical science to FDA approved drugs and diagnostics.

1.2 Overview of Drug Discovery and Development

Kevin Grimes

Drug discovery and development is not for the faint of heart. The bar is indeed high for a new molecule to receive regulatory approval for widespread clinical use—and appropriately so. As patients, we want our drugs to be both safe and effective. The failure rate in drug development is quite high. Only 20% of drugs entering clinical study receive regulatory approval and the failure rate is even higher during the preclinical phase of development. Given the complex array of drug-like behaviors that the new molecule must exhibit and the large number of interdependent tasks that must be successfully accomplished during development, this high rate of attrition is not unexpected.

The development cost for each successful drug is staggering, ranging from several hundred million to several billion dollars. The latter figure typically includes the cost of failed programs and the cost of capital. While an exceptionally well-executed program may be completed within 7 years, the norm is closer to 12 years and often much longer. Since patent protection for a new compound is granted for 20 years, the period of exclusive marketing after regulatory approval is typically in the range of 7–8 years, leaving a relatively short time for recovery of costs and generation of profit.

1.2.1 The Shifting Landscape

We are currently in a time of transition in the biopharmaceutical sector. The number of pharmaceutical companies has contracted through mergers and acquisitions as larger companies seek to fill their pipelines. Many profitable drugs are facing their "patent cliff." The "blockbuster" business model, which favored development of drugs for very large markets (statins, antihypertensives, drugs for type 2 diabetes, etc.), is falling into disfavor as advances in "omics" allow for more tailored patient therapies. The previously ignored orphan diseases (<200,000 patients in the USA) recently became more attractive for several reasons: (1) regulatory incentives effectively guarantee a period of marketing exclusivity, (2) clinical development costs can be substantially lower, and (3) "designer drugs" can command a premium in pricing.

Biopharmaceutical companies have drastically cut their basic research staffs because of pressures to decrease costs in order to improve profits. The number of biotechnology venture funds is contracting, especially those that will invest in new biopharmaceutical start-up companies. As a result, we can expect that fewer novel drug programs will originate in the biopharmaceutical sector.

Academics are well positioned to step into the breach, especially if there is institutional support for translational activities. This support can come through funding, the creation of core service centers (e.g., high throughput screening centers, medicinal chemistry units, animal imaging centers, phase 1 units, etc.), and a culture that values bringing new treatments to patients. By advancing our promising basic research discoveries towards novel therapies for unmet clinical needs, we academics will maintain our social contract with our fellow citizens who pay for our research and hope for better health in return. In addition, we will contribute to our economy when successful academic programs enter the commercial sector as either start-up companies or new programs in existing biopharmaceutical companies.

1.2.2 The Critical Path

In order to obtain market approval for a new drug, a number of complex steps must be successfully navigated (Fig. 1.1). While many of the steps must be accomplished sequentially (e.g., demonstration of safety in animals before study in humans), drug

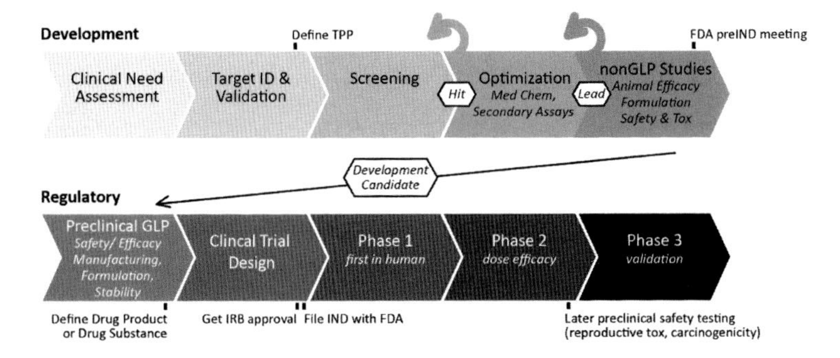

Fig. 1.1 General drug development pipeline. *TPP* Target Product Profile, *Med Chem* Medicinal Chemistry, *GLP* Good Laboratory Practice, *Tox* Toxicology, *FDA* Food and Drug Administration, *IND* Investigational New Drug application, *IRB* Institutional Review Board

development is very much an iterative process where a given step may be informed by or contingent upon many others. The following paragraphs provide an introduction to some of the critical steps in the development process. The timing of the handoff from academia to industry depends upon several factors, including cost of development and commercial attractiveness. For example, a repurposed drug may be fully developed within academia, whereas a more costly monoclonal antibody program may necessitate an earlier handoff in order to advance.

Box 1.6: Key Terms and Abbreviations

mAb: Monoclonal antibody
HTS: High-Throughput Screening
Hit: Molecules that display the desired activity in an assay
Lead: Most promising early-stage molecule(s) identified through *in vitro* and *in vivo* testing
Development candidate: Molecule selected for clinical development after meeting criteria established in the TPP for efficacy, pharmacokinetics, and safety
TPP: Target Product Profile; a document outlining desired characteristics of the final drug product
SAR: Structure–Activity Relationship
ADME: Absorption, Distribution, Metabolism, and Elimination; pharmacokinetic parameters
API: Active Pharmaceutical Ingredient
Drug Product: API and inactive components such as binders, capsule, etc. that compose the final drug formulation
Excipient: Inactive material added to the formulation to control drug dissolution, absorption, stability, etc.

(continued)

Box 1.6 (continued)

IND: Investigational New Drug application; document filed with the FDA prior to initiating research on human subjects using any drug that has not been previously approved for the proposed clinical indication, dosing regimen, or patient population
GLP: Good Laboratory Practice; extensive documentation of each procedural step to ensure high quality, reproducible studies
CRO: Contract Research Organization
FDA: US Food and Drug Administration
GMP: Good Manufacturing Practice; exacting procedures and documentation of quality assurance carried out at a certified facility (sometimes referred to as "cGMP" for "current" practice)
CMC: Chemistry, Manufacturing, and Controls
NDA: New Drug Application; FDA paperwork to obtain approval for the sales and marketing of a new drug in the USA
BLA: Biologics License Application; FDA paperwork to obtain approval for the sales and marketing of a new biologic in the USA

1.2.2.1 Identifying the Opportunity/Target

Academics have discovered promising new drugs through a variety of approaches. Serendipity has played a role, as when Alexander Fleming combined critical observation with scientific acumen to discover penicillin. Unexpected side effects in early clinical studies have also been used to therapeutic advantage. This is how the anti-angina/antihypertensive drug sildenafil was repurposed as the first drug in the lucrative erectile dysfunction market. More typically, however, academic drug discovery is biology-driven—the result of hard work at the research bench. Novel associations are uncovered between specific proteins (or protein mutations) or pathways and one or more underlying diseases. The causality must then be proven through target validation studies using gene knockout/knock-in models, siRNA gene silencing, or tool molecules that modulate the activity of the protein of interest.

1.2.2.2 Selecting the Therapeutic Approach

Once confidence in your target is established, it is time to consider the therapeutic approach. Most often, intracellular targets will require a small molecule approach, whereas cell surface targets (e.g., CD20) and circulating bioactive molecules (e.g., tumor necrosis factor) may be amenable to monoclonal antibody (mAb) approaches as well. Some advantages to mAb therapeutics include the more predictable safety profile, less frequent dosing, and premium pricing. Disadvantages include the need for parenteral (intravenous) dosing and the higher early development costs, a major drawback for academic researchers. Some diseases are best addressed by replacing deficient hormones (e.g., thyroxin for hypothyroidism) or bioactive proteins (e.g., glucocerebrosidase in Gaucher's disease or erythropoietin for anemia associated with kidney failure).

1.2.2.3 Assessing Clinical Need

Before embarking on an expensive and time-consuming development plan, it is important to ensure the therapy will provide a clinical benefit. Take an unbiased look at clinical need, the suitability of the approach, and the feasibility of clinical development. This is best accomplished by a comprehensive review of the relevant literature and by extensive discussions with clinical experts and disease advocacy groups. The goal is to develop an outline of the clinical development plan, including route of administration, dosing regimen, efficacy endpoints, and duration of the trials. Obtaining help from a clinical trial design expert and a regulatory consultant can ensure that the team is on the right path.

Once you have determined your clinical indication and therapeutic approach, it is imperative that your team establish a Target Product Profile (TPP). This critical document defines the essential characteristics of the final drug product and will serve as an important guide throughout the development process.

Box 1.7: What Surprised an Academician?

We—as academics—are often under the impression that drug development, unlike our own basic research, is a rather mundane and straightforward process. In fact, those of us who have spent time in the biopharmaceutical industry have found that drug discovery and development lies at the intersection of basic research and applied science and requires a great deal of creativity and rigor. Exceptional scientists populate both the biopharmaceutical industry and the regulatory agencies. Drug development can be every bit as challenging and require even more persistence than traditional academic research. *–DM-R*

1.2.2.4 Determining the Preclinical Animal Model

Unfortunately, rodents are much easier to cure than humans. A critical step in predicting the efficacy of the drug under development will be to select an appropriate animal model for the clinical indication. While animal models are only imperfect approximations of the clinical disease, some models are more analogous than others. We might recognize that the administration of a neurotoxin to produce acute Parkinsonism in rodents has little similarity to chronic Parkinson disease, which progresses over many years in patients. But we currently do not have better models. We might predict that occlusion of the middle cerebral artery in a rat would closely approximate a stroke in humans caused by acute occlusion of the same vessel. But multiple new drugs that showed efficacy in rodent stroke models failed to show benefit in humans.

There are many reasons for this lack of predictive value. In preclinical *in vivo* studies, the strains are typically inbred. The study animals are relatively young and frequently of one sex. They are fed the same food and follow the same sleep-wake cycles. Human subjects have diverse genetic backgrounds, and come from a wider range of ages (often older) of both genders. Furthermore, human patients eat a varied diet, follow varied lifestyles, and may be taking a number of concomitant medications that could interfere with the new drug's absorption, metabolism, mechanism of action, or apparent treatment effect.

1.2.2.5 Defining the Drug Candidate

In the case of small molecules, this typically requires designing a chemical or cell-based assay to identify activators or inhibitors of a target, and then optimizing the assay for use in a high throughput screening (HTS) facility. Most HTS centers have libraries containing between 10^5 and 10^6 compounds. Generally, a successful HTS will identify a few families of related molecules that have activity against the target of interest at low micromolar concentrations. An experienced medicinal chemist can help exclude certain *hits* as false positives that either interfere with the reporter in the assay or exhibit exceptional promiscuity in targets. Those compounds that appear to be true hits can then be validated in a secondary screen. The most promising of these will become the *lead* molecule.

Once the team is satisfied that the lead compound truly modulates the target, a medicinal chemist can suggest chemical modifications to help optimize the desired molecular features, including potency (ideally activity in low nanomolar concentrations), selectivity for the desired target, solubility, bioavailability, duration of action, protein binding, plasma half life, etc. This SAR analysis is an iterative process involving new chemical modifications and biologic testing to identify the most promising compound. The goal is to identify a drug that meets acceptable standards for efficacy, toxicology, pharmacokinetics/ADME (absorption, distribution, metabolism, and excretion); as well as a wide therapeutic window (ratio of toxic dose/minimally efficacious dose). This process should culminate in designating a *development candidate*, or active pharmaceutical ingredient (API) that meets pre-defined advancement criteria in the TPP.

The final *drug product* will include not only the API but also excipients to help maintain stability (shelf life), control dissolution rate, and otherwise optimize performance of the drug. Certain salts of the API may provide better solubility characteristics than others. Once the optimized formulation that we intend to bring forward into clinical studies has been identified, we can proceed with the more expensive IND-enabling preclinical studies.

1.2.2.6 IND-Enabling Preclinical Studies

Once the drug product has been finalized, it is time to begin to design and execute a series of rigorous preclinical studies that will characterize the safety, pharmacokinetics, ADME, and interactions with drugs that will be given concurrently in the clinic. These studies must be carried out under Good Laboratory Practice (GLP) and are typically conducted at a GLP contract research organization (CRO). GLP entails a good deal of quality control and documentation to ensure that the studies are carried out in exactly the manner as stated. The FDA provides guidance documents on its Web site regarding these studies, which must be completed before filing an Investigational New Drug application (IND) in order to begin a human clinical study. Because of the scope of work and documentation required, IND-enabling studies may cost in excess of 1 million dollars.

Prior to embarking on these expensive studies, it is prudent to arrange for a pre-IND meeting with the FDA. The goal is to obtain general concurrence on the development plan and to ask specific questions regarding the drug product, proposed clinical studies, and preclinical development plan. Since the animal toxicology studies must predict safety for the human studies, they must be similar in route of administration, dosing regimen, and duration. Therefore, seek some assurance that the proposed series of preclinical studies will be acceptable to the FDA.

During GLP toxicology studies, animals must be dosed for at least as long as the intended clinical studies, so the animal studies can only be designed after formalizing the clinical study design. The drug product used in preclinical studies must also be prepared according to GLP standards. Ideally, this GLP drug should be less pure than the clinical grade drug product that will eventually be dosed in patients. If the contrary were true, then animal toxicology studies would not adequately reflect safety for patients, because the increased impurities in the clinical drug will not have been tested in animals.

More expensive GLP reproductive toxicology, carcinogenicity, and long-term stability studies can often be deferred until before initiation of phase 3 clinical studies.

1.2.2.7 Obtaining GMP Drug Product

Drug product that will be used in the clinic must be manufactured and quality tested according to Good Manufacturing Practice (GMP). GMP manufacturing requires exacting procedures and documentation and must be carried out at an experienced and certified facility. In addition to the manufacturing procedures, strict quality testing is performed at set intervals (e.g., every 3 months) under a variety of conditions to ensure that the drug is of highest quality. The drug product is tested to ensure that the API has not degraded and that new impurities have not appeared. Parenteral formulations are also tested for sterility and for the presence of endotoxins. The GMP manufacturing process and quality testing are resource intensive and quite expensive, so it makes sense to obtain several quotes and enlist a

Chemistry, Manufacturing, and Controls (CMC) expert to evaluate the facilities under consideration. The FDA will often audit GMP facilities to ensure compliance.

1.2.2.8 Filing the IND

The IND contains three major sections. The clinical section contains the clinical protocol for the phase 1 clinical trial as well as the investigator's brochure, which describes the drug in detail and reports possible safety issues based upon the preclinical animal safety studies. The preclinical section reports the results of the GLP studies and any additional information that may be relevant to safety. The CMC section contains information regarding the API, formulation, manufacturing process, and quality control studies. Once the IND has been submitted, the FDA has 30 days to respond with concerns, or clinical studies in humans may commence.

1.2.2.9 Clinical Development

Phase 1 studies are *first in human* studies primarily conducted to characterize the pharmacokinetics and determine the safety in people. Most often, phase 1 studies are conducted in healthy volunteers. Occasionally, they are carried out in patients who stand to possibly benefit if the drug carries significant risk of adverse effects (e.g., neutropenia) or must be administered in an invasive manner (e.g., intracoronary or intraventricular). For example, cancer patients are often the subjects of phase 1 studies of chemotherapeutic agents since these drugs typically produce serious side effects.

Phase 2 studies are performed to explore the effective dose range or dosing regimen and to demonstrate efficacy. Often, the primary endpoint in phase 2 proof-of-concept studies is a surrogate biomarker associated with disease progression rather than a clinical endpoint, since the latter would require a much larger study to reach statistical significance. For example, when studying a new drug for chronic heart failure, the study might be powered to demonstrate a difference in ejection fraction on serial echocardiograms rather than a change in the composite of hospitalizations and death. Once adequate efficacy is demonstrated for surrogate endpoints and the best dose(s) determined, the drug is ready for the pivotal phase 3 studies.

Phase 3 studies are larger studies that are powered to clinical endpoints that are acceptable to the FDA. Typically two separate studies with an efficacy p-value of <0.05 are required for final drug registration. If the drug addresses a serious unmet need, the FDA might allow a single study with a lower p-value (e.g., <0.01). Assuming phase 3 studies demonstrate both safety and efficacy, it is now time to compile the data into a New Drug Application (NDA) or Therapeutic Biologic Application (BLA) and submit to the FDA. Review of this final submission may take up to 18 months. If the project has Fast Track designation for a drug that addresses a serious unmet need, the review may be completed in 10 months. The FDA may request that an Advisory Committee comprised of external experts make a recommendation regarding final market approval, although the FDA may concur or disagree with the Advisory Committee's recommendation. Once an approval is granted, we are free to market our drug in compliance with FDA regulations.

Box 1.8: The Bottom Line

Drug discovery and development is a complex process involving many interdependent disciplines. Success requires creativity, persistence, some degree of luck, and a willingness to enlist the aid of experts in various fields.

1.3 Assessing Clinical Need

Kevin Grimes

As academic drug developers, we hope to translate our ideas into effective new therapies that will save lives, improve health and quality of life, and/or lower the costs of health care. We arrive at our therapeutic approaches in different ways. We may be basic research scientists who have discovered a promising new cellular target or pathway that plays a critical role in one or more serious diseases of which we have only a superficial clinical knowledge. Or we may be physician scientists or basic researchers who have dedicated our career to finding a cure for a specific disease with which we are intimately familiar. In either case, we need to call upon the collective wisdom of our peers, disease experts, and experts in drug development to ensure that our therapeutic approach will address the unmet needs of the patients in an optimal manner; and the unmet needs are great.

Despite impressive advances in drug therapy over the past 50 years, tremendous numbers of patients are in desperate need of effective new therapies for a wide variety of medical conditions. The list of diseases with inadequate or no treatments is daunting. Consider the following examples: pediatric diseases such as sickle cell disease, inborn errors of metabolism, bullous skin diseases, and autism spectrum disorders; obstetric disorders including premature birth and preeclampsia; global health challenges such as multi-drug resistant tuberculosis, chronic Chagas' disease, and newly emerging viral diseases; autoimmune conditions including progressive systemic sclerosis (scleroderma), systemic lupus erythematosis, and multiple sclerosis; neurodegenerative conditions such as amyotrophic lateral sclerosis, Huntington's disease, and Alzheimer's disease; and a wide variety of intractable malignancies. These examples are just the tip of the iceberg.

1.3.1 Starting with the End in Mind

Before we embark on a lengthy and costly campaign to develop a new drug, it is imperative that we understand why patients and providers will use our proposed product. What clinical problem are we solving? What specific unmet medical need will our product address? How will patients or the health care system be better off once our new drug is available? Are there known or predictable risks involved with modulating our drug's molecular target, and if so, is the risk-to-benefit ratio acceptable to our intended patient population? Will our drug delivery and dosing approach be acceptable to patients and providers? Will payers (insurers, health plans, Medicare, Medicaid) agree to pay for our new therapy?

1.3.2 Understanding Clinical Need

The first step is to understand the unmet clinical need. There are numerous reasons why a new therapeutic might be needed for a given condition. The following categories provide a framework for analyzing the necessity for a new drug for a clinical indication.

1.3.2.1 No Therapies Currently Available

Clinical need is most apparent when there are no effective treatments for a serious disease. Amyotrophic lateral sclerosis and advanced pancreatic adenocarcinoma are clear examples where current drug therapy has little to offer except palliation.

1.3.2.2 Need to Reverse or Arrest the Disease Process

For other serious diseases, we have therapies that reduce symptoms temporarily and even prolong life, but do not arrest disease progression. For example, current drugs for Parkinson's disease improve neurologic symptoms and improve quality of life, but do not prevent the relentless downhill course of the disease. Similarly, current therapies for idiopathic pulmonary artery hypertension are vasodilators that do not arrest progression of the underlying pathology. Although therapies are available for such diseases, there is a tremendous need for novel drugs that will modify the progression of the disease.

1.3.2.3 Severe/Unacceptable Side Effects

For many other diseases, current treatments may be effective, but cause serious or unwanted side effects. A few illustrative examples follow: (1) Hodgkin lymphoma was once a fatal disease, but can now be cured in the majority of cases using a combination of chemotherapy and radiation therapy. Despite this success, patients frequently develop delayed, but life-threatening cardiac toxicity from doxorubicin, one of the first-line chemotherapy drugs. (2) Corticosteroids can be life-saving treatments for a wide variety of autoimmune, allergic, or inflammatory diseases.

Yet they cause a litany of very harmful side effects. (3) The calcineurin inhibitors cyclosporine and tacrolimus, important components of immunosuppressive regimens following organ transplantation, can cause nephrotoxicity. Unfortunately, these drugs often damage the transplanted kidneys that they are protecting from the host immune system.

Many other very commonly prescribed medications cause unwanted side effects that affect the patient's health, quality of life, and even willingness to adhere to the drug regimen. Selective serotonin reuptake inhibitor (SSRI) and serotonin–-norepinephrine reuptake inhibitor (SNRI) antidepressants commonly cause sedation, weight gain or loss, and sexual dysfunction. Metoclopramide, the most commonly prescribed drug for diabetic gastroparesis (delayed gastric emptying), can cause extrapyramidal movement disorders including irreversible tardive dyskinesia. Clearly, patients would benefit tremendously from effective drugs that lack such undesirable side effects.

1.3.2.4 Patient Preference/Convenience/Cost

In general, oral drugs that require less frequent dosing are preferable and improve patient adherence. Physicians rarely prescribe oral erythromycin (dosed four times daily for 7–10 days) since the FDA-approved azithromycin (dosed once daily for 5 days). Some drugs must be administered intravenously at an infusion center, which is both inconvenient and costly. Alternative treatments that a patient can dose at home would be preferable.

Many new therapies, especially biological drugs, are prohibitively expensive. Less costly drugs would be a terrific boon to patients, insurers, and the health care system. New platforms for biological drug discovery, development, and manufacturing might increase the success, shorten the time lines, and lower the costs of new therapies.

1.3.3 Suitability of Approach

After studying the unmet clinical need, our second step is to determine whether our planned therapeutic approach will provide an acceptable solution. For example, a peptide therapeutic that is injected subcutaneously twice a day might be readily acceptable for treating cancer, but is a non-starter for male pattern baldness. Speaking with physician experts, patient advocacy groups, patients, and eventually the FDA (and other regulatory agencies) will help us identify the acceptable and ideal drug characteristics.

Box 1.9: What Surprised an Academician?

When we proposed developing a new treatment for the prevention of radiation dermatitis (the skin burn that occurs as a result of radiation therapy for malignant tumors), we were surprised when a potential investor insisted that there was no unmet clinical need in this indication. His dermatology expert reported that he never saw patients with this problem. But since dermatologists do not have any effective treatments, the radiologists no longer make referrals and instead prescribe emollients to try to alleviate this very debilitating condition. In fact, there is significant unmet need; the burns of radiation dermatitis cause substantial suffering and frequently require that further radiation be withheld. Our lesson: Cast a wide net—make sure you are speaking with the right experts, and with patients too. *–DM-R*

In the case of a serious or life-threatening disease that currently lacks an effective treatment, there will be a higher tolerance for side effects, patient inconvenience, and associated costs. Let us suppose our new drug is expected to arrest or reverse the progression of Huntington's disease. Patients would very likely be willing to accept an increased risk of serious side effects such as cardiac arrhythmias. They would probably also be willing to use the drug even if it required subcutaneous, intravenous, or even intrathecal administration in the doctor's office. And certainly, a drug that prevented the death and disability of Huntington's disease could command premium pricing.

Now let us suppose we are developing a novel therapeutic for a less serious condition—a new drug that prevents cataract formation. Since cataract surgery is effective, safe, and quite inexpensive, our new drug must have minimal side effects, convenient oral or topical dosing, and low cost if we expect patients, providers, and payers to support its use. We should also recognize that ophthalmologists might be less likely to champion our drug since it will severely undercut the number of surgeries they perform.

1.3.4 Feasibility of Development

Our next step is to determine whether it is feasible to develop our new drug. Is there a straightforward clinical development path? What is our target subject (patient) population? What are the primary and secondary endpoint(s)? How long must we follow the subjects to show efficacy for this endpoint? Are there predictive surrogate endpoints that we can follow? How large is our anticipated effect size? How many subjects must be enrolled? Can we afford to conduct this trial? To answer these questions, we should start with a comprehensive review of the medical literature regarding clinical trials in our indication. We should then speak with physician experts in our chosen disease as well as clinical trial design experts and biostatisticians.

Lastly, we should try to understand the competition in our therapeutic area. What new therapies are in the development pipeline for our chosen indication? What are their mechanisms of action? Do they target the same patient population? If a pharmaceutical company has a 2 year head start using our same approach, perhaps we should move on to another clinical indication or another research project. We can explore the competition by doing the following:

1. Search the clinicaltrials.gov Web site for ongoing clinical trials in our clinical indication.
2. Search the pharmaceutical industry trade journals for novel drugs in our therapeutic area—these periodicals may be readily available through your university's business school library.
3. Search the internet for similar activity.
4. Speak with health care investors and other members of the biotechnology/pharmaceutical community to obtain non-confidential information about potential competitors.

On occasion, we may find that it is feasible to develop our drug for a number of clinical indications. In this case, we should not necessarily pursue the indication with the largest market size. Rather, we should determine which clinical development path has the surest and fastest route to regulatory approval. Once our drug is on the market, we can expand to other indications as part of the "life-cycle management" of the drug.

Box 1.10: The Bottom Line

Abraham Lincoln, arguably the greatest leader in the history of the United States, once said, "If I had eight hours to chop down a tree, I'd spend six sharpening my axe." Before spending our valuable time and resources executing a new drug development project, we must be certain that:

1. We are advancing an optimized product that addresses the needs of patients
2. We have a clear path forward
3. Our approach will still be valued by patients, physicians, and payers when it is finally ready for clinical adoption

1.4 Target Product Profile (TPP)

Robert Lum

A Target Product Profile, or TPP, is a list of attributes and minimum acceptable criteria that a project team should strive to meet when developing a new drug. The TPP provides a general set of goals for the project, but the more specific it can be made, the more useful it becomes. TPPs can and should be refined over time as new information becomes available, thus allowing the profile to be used as a guidance document, driving the research effort and keeping the team focused on the program's ultimate goals. The examples given below are not complete TPPs, but present relevant parts of a profile. Since each project is different, each TPP will have specific criteria that are tailored to each individual development program.

Box 1.11: Key Terms and Abbreviations

TPP: Target Product Profile; a document outlining desired characteristics of the final drug product
mAb: monoclonal antibody
PK/ADME: pharmacokinetics/absorption, distribution, metabolism, elimination; studies of how the body processes drugs
SI: sensitivity index
IC_{50}: drug concentration required to inhibit a process by half its full activity
ip: intraperitoneal (within the abdominal cavity)
po: oral administration
hERG: ion channel cell-based screen for cardiac toxicity
IP: intellectual property
PFS: progression free survival

TPPs are refined at various stages of the drug development process. At the onset of a project, the criteria can be general, and the TPP is used to guide the overall direction of the project and set "go/no go" decision points to continue project development. Defining a TPP also forces the team to think about attributes outside of their area of expertise. General characteristics of therapeutics include the clinical indication, route and frequency of administration, medical need, competition, current therapy, cost of intended therapy, stability, clinical development path, regulatory path, and IP position. This can be a daunting list of categories to consider, but it is important to remember that the team will refine broad characterizations into narrow specification windows as development progresses. SPARK uses a general template to get the process started (Table 1.1).

Table 1.1 SPARK target product profile template

Category	Final characteristics (ideal and acceptable ranges)
Product description	– Type of agent (small molecule, peptide, mAb) – Proposed target
Indication and usage	– Clinical Indication(s)—if more than one, specify intended lead indication – Intended patient population – Current available treatment options (including surgical, lifestyle, and homeopathic options)
Development candidate	– Target specificity – Efficacy (*in vitro*, cell-based, and *in vivo*)
Preclinical work	– Animal model(s) of disease – Safety/toxicity profiles
Clinical pharmacology	– Absorption, distribution, metabolism, excretion – Half-life in plasma or serum – Pharmacodynamics (extent of target inhibition or activation) – Protein binding, etc.
Dosage and administration	– Dosing amount, frequency, etc. – Route of Administration – Formulation (excipients) – Estimated shelf life, required storage conditions, etc.
Safety and toxicity in humans	– Known on-target or off-target predicted safety concerns – Therapeutic window
Regulatory considerations	– Presumed clinical path forward – Eligibility for Orphan drug status, Fast Track, Subpart H, etc. – Precedents set by previous trials in indication/patient population
Intellectual property	– Freedom to operate evaluation (competing patents, opportunities to write new patents) – Desired licensing outcome (license to company vs. start-up)
Financial considerations	– Cost of goods – Projected pricing and affordability compared to current options – Cost to develop – Estimated return on investment

Considering these attributes ahead of time allows the project team to map the path to meet the goals, determine additional expertise that may be needed, and prioritize what needs to get done in the context of the overall program. Example 1 provides a brief TPP that defines the general goals of a program.

Example 1: General TPP for Uncomplicated Falciparum Malaria

Adapted from Frearson et al. [1]:

1. Oral dosing (ideally once, but not more than 3 times per day)
2. Low cost of goods (~US $1 per full course of treatment)
3. Effective against drug resistant parasites (e.g., those that have developed resistance to chloroquine or sulfadoxine–pyrimethamine treatment)
4. Fast acting and curative within 3 days
5. Potential for combination with other agents

6. Pediatric formulation should be available
7. Stable under tropical conditions
8. IP: requires freedom to operate; composition of matter patent would be ideal

When developing a new chemical entity, the team uses the TPP to guide their efforts to optimize the characteristics of the lead molecule. The TPP document might include, for example, minimum acceptable criteria for the biochemical assays, cell-based assays, functional assays, selectively assays, solubility, size (molecular weight), chirality, toxicity profile, formulation, genotoxicity studies, safety pharmacology assays, maximum tolerated dose, efficacy in certain animal models, pharmacokinetic parameters, and intellectual property position. As the program matures, additional criteria may be added, such as pharmacokinetics/ pharmacodynamics relationships, metabolic profile, frequency of dosing, number of animal models needed to be tested, and additional toxicity studies. The team has to define the desired parameters for each attribute. Once all of the criteria are met, a final set of compounds can be compared and the lead compound selected as a clinical development candidate. Example 2 provides a research-oriented TPP, with specific criteria for preclinical testing.

Box 1.12: What Surprised an Academician?

At first, we did not understand the value of establishing explicit criteria in a TPP. After all, we knew where we were going. Why waste time stating the obvious? But defining essential characteristics in a TPP has proven to be essential; it mapped our path, identified whom we needed to engage, and established optimal attributes for our product. *–DM-R*

Example 2: Hit-to-Lead TPP for Protozoa and Helminth Disease

Adapted from Nwaka et al. [2]:

1. *In vitro* activity in antiprotozoan screens:
   Plasmodium falciparum: IC_{50} <0.2 μg/mL
   Trypansoma cruzi: IC_{50} <1.0 μg/mL.
2. Antihelminthic screens:
   Schistosoma mansoni: 100% adult worm motility reduction, IC_{50} <2 μg/mL
   Onochocerca lienalis, *O. ochengi*, or *O. volvulus*: 100% inhibition of microfilarial motility at 1.25×10^{-5} M or 10 μg/mL.
3. Established selectivity for a molecular target or differential sensitivity between parasite and host enzymes should be > ten-fold.
4. Pre-toxicity screen in non-infected mice using up to 100 mg/kg ip or po.
5. *In vivo* activity in mouse or hamster models: significant reduction in parasitemia and/or increase in life span at 4×50 mg/kg either through ip or po route with no overt signs of toxicity.
6. Metabolic stability determined in microsomes in at least two species, including humans.

7. hERG binding >10 μM.
8. Low CYP450 inhibition profile.
9. IP: should be novel and be able to file for composition of matter patent.

During clinical development, the TPP should be modified to help define more clinically relevant attributes. This includes the primary indication, patient subtypes, dosing regimens, clinical pharmacokinetics, numbers of patients needed, clinical endpoints, cost of goods, and marketing or commercial strategy. The TPP can also define regulatory strategy, research into companion diagnostics, and alternate therapeutic indications or formulations. Example 3 provides a TPP for a compound in clinical development that may be used to guide the program team during the clinical development phase.

Example 3: Clinical Development TPP for a Clinical Stage Glioblastoma Cancer Drug

Adapted from unpublished program

1. Population: Seek approval alone or in combination with bevacizumab for the treatment of glioblastoma multiforme which has progressed after treatment with radiation plus temozolomide.
2. Efficacy: Median Progression Free Survival (PFS) >6.3 months compared with 4.2 months for bevacizumab alone; Median overall survival >9 months for combination.
3. Safety: Grade 3 or 4 neutropenia assumed in majority of patients; manageable with growth factor support. Neuropathy Grade 3 or 4 in <10% of patients. Other toxicities manageable, predictable, and reversible.
4. Dosing: 120 mg/m^2 IV once every 3 weeks until disease progression or 6 cycles.
5. IP: seek patent protection for novel combination therapy with bevacizumab.
6. Sustainable supply chain with cost of goods: <$50 per vial.

Box 1.13: The Bottom Line

The TPP should define the desired attributes of the novel therapeutic under development and should be edited and refined as the product moves further through the development pipeline. An effective TPP includes: clinical indication and medical need; route and frequency of administration; current and future competition; cost of intended therapy; intellectual property position; and all other advantages over current treatments. Other possible attributes include clinical development path; regulatory path; and metabolic and safety profiles.

1.5 Project Management and Project Planning

Rebecca Begley and Daria Mochly-Rosen

As academics, we take for granted that we know how to staff and manage our laboratories and/or clinics. Most members of our research teams are fairly junior and are trained in similar disciplines. The principal investigator is the leader and sets the research agenda. Progress is not usually tracked against a formal timeline and the research plan can rapidly change direction to pursue new and interesting observations. Little attention is given to actively managing the research enterprise per se.

But in industry, project management is a highly valued function that substantially increases the likelihood of a successful outcome and saves both time and money. Project teams bring together individuals with varying levels of seniority and widely divergent areas of expertise, such as pharmacology, toxicology, regulatory science, drug manufacturing, and clinical trial design (referred to as cross-functional teams). Team members are committed to advancing their project in a timely and collaborative manner. They are also encouraged to kill a project as soon as possible if the research indicates that the project is unlikely to succeed or will incur unacceptable costs or delays.

Box 1.14: Key Terms and Abbreviations

Gantt chart: development plan tracking tool listing critical tasks, timelines, and dependencies
Cross-functional team: project team comprised of individuals with expertise in different areas (e.g., pharmacology, ADME, manufacturing, regulatory science, clinical) required for successful completion of the project
TPP: Target Product Profile; a document outlining desired characteristics of the final drug product
CRO: Contract Research Organization
IND: Investigational New Drug application; document filed with the FDA prior to initiating research on human subjects using any drug that has not been previously approved for the proposed clinical indication, dosing regimen, or patient population

1.5.1 Project Leadership

Project management requires strong leadership, a committed team with the necessary complement of skills, and a well thought out development plan. The project team works together to identify the project's strategy (vision), goals (tactics), and a detailed plan of execution. The project leader then helps keep the team on task at the budget and timeline that were predetermined.

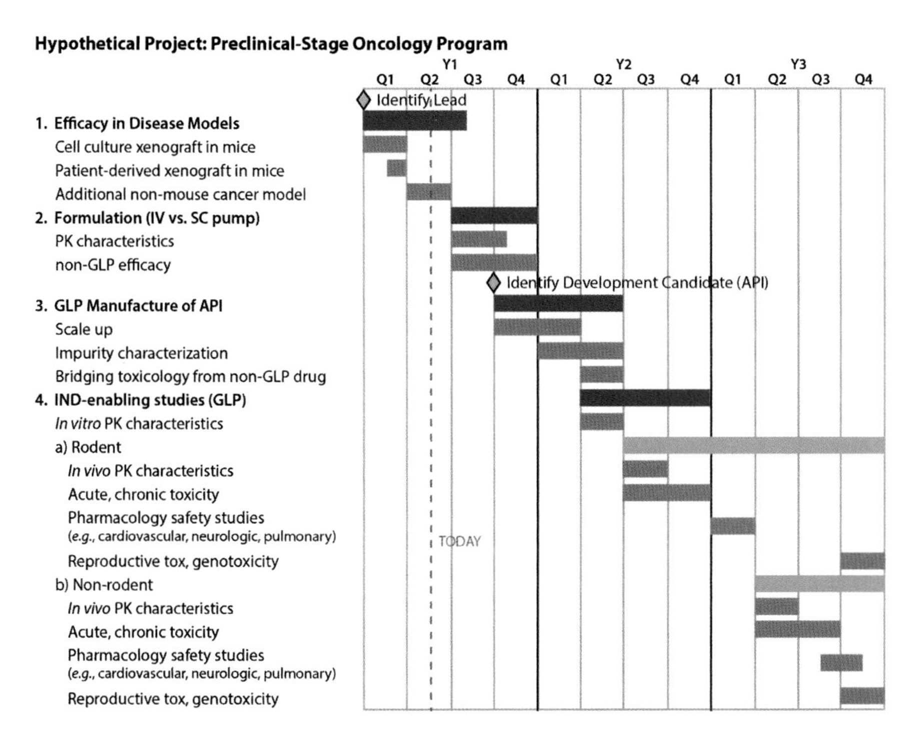

Fig. 1.2 Theoretical Gantt Chart for a preclinical-stage oncology program. This project Gantt Chart outlines possible tasks and predicted timelines for a hypothetical development program. *Q* Quarter, *Y* Year, *IV* intravenous, *SC* subcutaneous, *PK* pharmacokinetic, *GLP* Good Lab Practices, *API* Active Pharmaceutical Ingredient, *IND* Investigational New Drug application, *tox* toxicology

Importantly, many of the tasks carried out by the team members are highly interdependent. For example, drug supply for a clinical study cannot be manufactured until the appropriate clinical dosing regimen(s) is worked out. Clinical dosing for a first-in-human trial is furthermore highly dependent upon the toxicology, pharmacokinetics, and efficacy found in animal studies.

A Gantt chart is a very useful tool that provides a detailed road map for executing and tracking the development project. It includes a comprehensive listing of each task that must be accomplished during the project, along with its anticipated timeline and its dependencies upon other parts of the project (see Fig. 1.2). The project manager can use the Gantt chart to track the progress of each task as well as overall progress of the project against the desired timeline. Similarly, team members representing different functional areas can track their tasks and see how slippage in their timeline might affect the overall timeline. For example, a delay in delivery of acceptable quality drug product will delay the start of IND-enabling toxicology studies and, in turn, delay the filing of the IND. That may seem obvious, but if we are late we also risk losing our time slot at the contract research organization (CRO) conducting the toxicology studies, which would cost us money in penalty payments to the CRO and further delay development. The costs and consequences of small delays can quickly snowball in drug development.

The Gantt chart is not set in stone and should be revised by the project manager to reflect reality as new information becomes available. Although complications invariably arise during drug development, the Gantt chart is an extremely useful instrument to help the development team complete the project on a timeline that fits the company's goals.

1.5.2 Project Management for SPARK

We include a section on project management because academics engaged in translational research must take on this function to ensure timely and successful completion of their aims. The project leader may be the faculty member, but can also be a student or a fellow. The team may include expert advisors, other research laboratories at the institution or elsewhere, as well as commercial research services (e.g., medicinal chemistry or toxicology). The team members in this case are not bound in the same way that they are in our own lab or in a typical project team in a company. Further, it is unlikely that the project leader will be able to assemble all the function heads for a meeting; therefore, a lot of the project planning relies on coordination and individual conversations with each expert and function. When possible, it is advisable to share the plan details with all the members of the team to confirm assumptions and coordinate progression. The following section and suggested references provide some practical advice on leading cross-functional teams; not all of it may apply to academic work [3, 4].

1.5.3 Leading a Cross-Functional Team

How to lead when you are not the expert or the most senior person in the team:

- Influence without authority depends on relationships and shared vision. Build the relationships before you need them.
- Stay flexible; adjust to new data or change in circumstances.
- Know enough about each functional area's activities to converse intelligently. You should understand where the key issues may arise and why. Ask questions early; establish mentors/go-to people to gain basic understanding.
- Use the cross-functional team meetings as a forum for holding the entire team accountable to the project and each other.
- Use cross-functional team meetings also to identify and address issues that arise from within each function as well as from an interface with another function (e.g., as discussed above, a delay in drug supply could impact the timing of a toxicology study).

- One way to gain agreement on contentious issues can be through pre-meeting discussions with key stakeholders, allowing them time to work through issues and voice opinions in advance of meeting.
- Written documentation can be useful for management of a team. Writing down goals and targets provides a common point of reference for communication, both internally within the team, as well as to external audiences. In addition, gaining team agreement on a written document can encourage more attention to the wording (written agreements can carry more weight than spoken ones) and subsequently can facilitate a greater degree of group buy-in, if the group feels involved in the process.
- Tools for communication can include the target product profile, the team goals and the team timelines/budget. Document assumptions as these will likely evolve over time.

Box 1.15: What Surprised an Academician?

A Gantt chart is rarely used in academia to identify specific goals and track progress towards them. Who can plan basic research with such detail? When asked to participate in this planning, I felt that it was a waste of time. I quickly realized that such detailed planning is an effective tool to create priorities, to know when to "kill a project" (e.g., it will be completed too late to impact the company's future, or the technical setback is so substantial that it is too expensive to complete), how to keep the project moving on track, and how to take corrective actions when budgets and/or timelines change. *–DM-R*

1.5.4 Aspects of Project Planning

Step 1: Plan with the end in mind—define the vision of the project.

We need to define a target product profile (TPP) with the team. This defines how our product will look and behave and will also define why a physician or patient would use our new drug by highlighting where it addresses unmet need. The "must-have" characteristics outlined in the TPP define the threshold below which the project would not be carried forwards and the project should be "killed." Published clinical trial data and product labels are resources for comparative information on related products.

Step 2: Outline a clinical development plan.

We need to hold an open discussion with the functional area leads to lay out a development plan. This is important even for an early stage project; broad strokes descriptions will suffice for the later stage activities. The development plan outlines decision points in the overall project development and details the activities needed to get from the current state to the next decision making point. In addition, the key risks and assumptions for the project are summarized. This activity is usually structured by starting with the TPP and working backwards to the current stage of development.

We start by asking the clinical lead to propose a clinical program that could support the desired indication laid out in the TPP. We should begin with the phase 3 studies, then ask what the preceding phase 2 and phase 1 studies would have to look like to support dose selection and study design for the phase 3 described. These discussions should help define variables such as endpoints, duration of treatment, number of doses, size of study, etc. As these are likely to change as the program evolves, test the boundaries of the proposed numbers. For example, if the clinician recommends that we treat this patient population for 1 month to see a significant change in a particular endpoint, we should query how likely it is that we would end up treating for 2 months or if it would be feasible to treat for 2 weeks instead. The rest of the team (toxicology, manufacturing, pharmacology, etc.) should be asked to propose activities that would be needed from their areas to support the clinical program as it is described. These activities should answer "key questions" that exist for the project.

Step 3: Lay out the project plan with all details to facilitate decision-making.

We need to place activities from the conversation in step 2 into a timeline, and include budget information. Many variables were likely discussed; it is best to pick a set that makes sense. Document the assumptions used to pull together this particular plan and ensure all envisioned activities needed to support the project are included.

Step 4: Define the activities needed to reach the next decision making point and set the goals accordingly.

As we review the overall project plan, inclusive of all proposed activities, we can prioritize the activities and determine which will add the most value to the project upon completion. For example, writing a clinical study protocol may add some value to the project, but completing a phase 1 study and having the data in hand will add significantly more value to the project. Then, we can evaluate the activities that could be done against the available budget.

We need to decide which activities the team will support moving forward (with a focus on the must-haves as first priority). These activities will comprise the goals (defined as things that add value) of the team. This list of goals becomes the project plan. We should revisit the plan upon receipt of new data or a change in the project environment (e.g., approval of a new agent in the disease indication, etc.)

Box 1.16: The Bottom Line

The development plan is an essential map for the team, navigating us through the many interdependent processes of drug development and defining critical "go/no go" decision points to continue or terminate the project. The plan is a living document without which we could wander off task, waste precious resources, and create delays in reaching our goal—to benefit patients.

References

1. Frearson JA, Wyatt PG, Gilbert IH, Fairlamb AH (2007) Target assessment for antiparasitic drug discovery. Trends Parasitol 23(12):589–595. doi:10.1016/j.pt.2007.08.019
2. Nwaka S, Ramirez B, Brun R, Maes L, Douglas F, Ridley R (2009) Advancing drug innovation for neglected diseases—criteria for lead progression. PLoS Negl Trop Dis 3(8):e440. doi:10.1371/journal.pntd.0000440
3. Kennedy A (2008) Pharmaceutical project management, vol 182, 2nd edn, Drugs and the pharmaceutical sciences. Informa Healthcare, New York
4. Linberg SE (2006) Expediting drugs and biologics development, 3rd edn. Parexel International Corporation, Waltham, MA, USA

Chapter 2
Discovery and Preclinical Work

Daria Mochly-Rosen and Kevin Grimes

In any drug discovery and development effort, we must accomplish a number of critical steps to arrive at a compound that is safe and efficacious, and also exhibits the complex array of desired drug-like behaviors that warrants advancement to the clinic. These tasks include target identification and validation; screening for active compounds; chemical modification of candidate compounds to achieve optimized pharmacology; formulating the final drug product; and establishing safety in preclinical models. "Repurposing" drugs that have previously been approved (or shown to be safe in humans) for new clinical indications can provide a faster, less risky, and more cost-effective route for bringing a new therapy to patients. Such shortcuts in development can be particularly valuable to resource-constrained academicians. When performing drug discovery research, we must be particularly attentive to the robustness of our experiments, because inability to reproduce academic data continues to be a sticking point when projects are transferred to industry. Our experiments must be appropriately blinded, statistically powered, and meticulously documented so that our findings are worthy of the large investment required for their further translation into a drug. This chapter walks through the essential preclinical drug development steps that lead to a clinical drug candidate.

D. Mochly-Rosen (✉)
Chemical and Systems Biology, Stanford University School of Medicine, 269 Campus Drive, Center for Clinical Science Research Rm 3145a, Stanford, CA 94305-5174, USA
e-mail: sparkmed@stanford.edu

K. Grimes
Chemical and Systems Biology, Stanford University School of Medicine, 269 Campus Drive, Center for Clinical Science Research Rm 3145c, Stanford, CA 94305-5174, USA
e-mail: kgrimes@stanford.edu

D. Mochly-Rosen and K. Grimes (eds.), *A Practical Guide to Drug Development in Academia*, SpringerBriefs in Pharmaceutical Science & Drug Development,
DOI 10.1007/978-3-319-02201-7_2, © The Editors 2014

2.1 Robustness of Preclinical Studies

Daria Mochly-Rosen

A number of recent commentaries challenge the robustness of academic preclinical studies. In one report, only 11% of published preclinical cancer studies from academic labs could be reproduced by Amgen scientists. This low rate was despite cooperation of the academic scientist who reported the original findings to reproduce the work at or with Amgen [1]. In another report, Bayer scientists found that ~75% of published academic studies brought in-house could not be reproduced, which resulted in termination of the effort to develop therapeutics based on these academic findings [2]. So what is going on?

The following discussion focuses on academic data related to animal studies. I will not repeat here the discussions of the importance of using the right animal models, how to confirm the findings using patient specimens, how to rely on proper understanding of pharmacokinetics and pharmacodynamics in using animal models, and how to the use proper "endpoints" for the studies. All these issues are discussed in later sections of this chapter. Instead, I focus on factors that may contribute to irreproducible animal data published by academicians and some simple measures to mitigate these issues.

Box 2.1: What Surprised an Academician?

In 2004, when I temporary moved from my academic lab to serve as the CSO of KAI Pharmaceuticals, I was hurt when our then CEO, who holds a B.A. in History, told me, "You will now learn that your academic work is not as robust as industry's standard." Like you, I take a great pride in our work in academia. I felt that conducting blinded studies, using several species, and reproducing the work in independent labs all combined to ensure high quality and valid data. That was not enough, I quickly learned. *–DM-R*

Box 2.2: Key Terms and Abbreviations

CSO: Chief Scientific Officer
Preclinical animal studies: animal studies done to validate a disease target and test the performance of a molecule prior to moving into human testing
***p*-value:** a statistical measure of the probability of obtaining a result at least as extreme as the one observed. If the *p*-value is less than the significance level (usually 0.05 or 0.01), one rejects the null hypothesis that there is no treatment effect
CDER: Center for Drug Evaluation and Research, within the Food and Drug Administration

(continued)

Box 2.2 (continued)

Endpoints: measurements (e.g., weight or tumor size) or observations (e.g., motor control or healthiness) used in a study to evaluate the effectiveness or safety of a treatment
Orphan indication: an FDA designation of a disease or condition that affects less than 200,000 people per year in the USA or for a treatment that is not expected to recoup its R&D costs due to pricing constraints
"me-toos": drugs that are approved after other chemically similar compounds or molecules with the same mechanism of action are already on the market

2.1.1 Factors that Contribute to Irreproducible Data

2.1.1.1 Heterogeneous Experimental Conditions

Animal studies can be greatly affected by many factors. Yet, often we do not give proper attention to these potentially confounding factors and/or we do not record the conditions used in detail. For example, rodents are nocturnal animals. Data related to their immune response, eating, exercise, ability to learn tasks, etc. are greatly affected by the time of day when the experiment is conducted. The chow feed is another important variable that can affect animal-derived data; some feed is rich in soy and therefore contributes feminizing hormones to both males and females. Variation in the feed may affect response to drug uptake and metabolism, to the integrity of the immune response, etc. Other confounding factors relate to the housing conditions, including noise, strong smells, and crowding; and a good animal facility should minimize them. Latent or full-blown infection by viruses, bacteria, mites, and other parasites can also affect the results of the study (See Box 2.3). All these variables should be held to a minimum and detailed information should be recorded so that even if there is no room to provide it in full in the publication, we will be able to share the specific conditions used during our study when contacted by a commercial entity or another academic laboratory.

Box 2.3: Lack of Reproducibility May Relate to Previously Unsuspected Confounding Factors

Lack of reproducibility of preclinical reports does not mean that the data are fabricated or wrong. One of the better-documented cases of inability to reproduce data in mice relates to the induction of type I diabetes in NOD mice. Initial claims attributed increased diabetes incidence reported by some groups to the difference in housing the mice in germ-free conditions.

(continued)

Box 2.3 (continued)

However, more recent data showed that intestinal microbiota are the critical confounding factor; presence of Bacillus cereus in the gut delayed onset, and reduced incidence of type-1 diabetes [3].

2.1.1.2 Bias and Incomplete Reporting

It is critical that the investigators who assess the animal data will be blinded to the experimental conditions; unintended bias can greatly affect the analysis, especially when the endpoint determinants are subjective.

Another problem with bias results from dismissing and not reporting negative or inconsistent data. The investigator may have a reasonable rationale for wanting to exclude data related to certain animals; we should include the rationale in the method section and let the readers draw their own conclusions. All the data (positive and negative) should be reported, as they may often help identify important variables to consider in human studies. For example, the observation that gender and age can affect the therapeutic response to drugs in models of heart attack in animals was not reported for a long time. When these findings were finally reported, reviewers started requesting preclinical studies include animals from both genders.

Box 2.4: Recommendations to Improve Robustness of Preclinical Studies (Expanded from Ref. [4])

1. Keep detailed information about the experimental conditions.
2. Keep detailed information on the source of all the reagents and lot numbers used in the study.
3. Seek advice of statisticians during the study design to ensure that the study is powered to address the question at hand, and that the appropriate statistical tests are applied.
4. Include appropriate negative controls and—when possible—positive controls for the study.
5. Have each study reproduced by another investigator in the lab, and in an independent lab if feasible.
6. The investigators should be blinded to the identity of the control and treatment groups during data analysis.
7. Provide information on all the animals that were included in the study, those that were excluded from the study and the reasons for the exclusion.
8. Validate reagents for the intended application (e.g., selectivity of small molecule, appropriate antibody for immunohistochemistry).

All studies should include both positive and negative controls. For example, a group of animals treated with a drug that was approved for this indication will enable a side-by-side comparison of the benefit of our intervention, as well as confirm that the disease model is relevant. Academics sometimes assume that certain controls are wasteful—"We have done these controls before" is a reasoning we often use. However, the control experiments need to be done side-by-side with the treatment arm, as unexpected factors can contribute to the outcome. A recent investigator in SPARK told us that they omitted an oral gavage of their control subjects before the last blood draw, only to discover later that gavage alone increases neutrophil number in the blood—possibly due to animal stress. Needless to say, the entire study had to be repeated.

It is important that critical experiments are repeated by a different investigator in the same lab to ensure that the experimental protocol is detailed enough to be reproduced by an unbiased researcher. When I first reported on the benefit after heart attack of treating animals with an inhibitor we developed for delta protein kinase C, the benefit was so surprising that one skeptic refused to believe the results. It was good to be able to answer that three members of the lab reproduced the same data. It was even better to be able to report that two other labs reproduced our data, and it was really a coup when that skeptic obtained the same data in his own laboratory.

2.1.1.3 Insufficient Statistical Power of the Study or Inappropriate Statistical Analysis

To save on animal use, researchers in academia often use too few animals per treatment group. Unfortunately, a p-value smaller than 0.05, although significant, is not robust enough if the study was done with 5 or less animals per treatment group.

If you are like me, you contact a statistician only when you try to analyze the data. A recent commentary urges academicians to recognize the critical contribution of statisticians in preclinical research [5]. Statisticians should be engaged early during the study planning to ensure that the number of animals included is sufficient and that the study is powered to provide an unequivocal answer. This will not only ease the review process, but importantly will increase the rigor of the study. Let us not have our budget dictate the number of animals per group we use, or we risk sacrificing the robustness of our results!

Biostatisticians can also weigh in on the appropriateness of the statistical tests used to analyze the results. Often, there is more than one statistical test available to compare groups, but characteristics of the data (e.g., size, distribution, etc.) may make some tests inappropriate. For example, we should not use a t-test on nonparametric data.

2.1.2 Conclusion

Given the Amgen and Bayer reproducibility studies, should we even attempt to do preclinical work in academia? Let us not throw the baby out with the bath water. Academic research provides essential fuel for new drug development, in general, and for orphan indications in particular. In a recent analysis of 252 drugs approved by CDER between 1998 and 2007, only 47% were considered scientifically novel; and academic discoveries contributed to a third of those novel molecules [6]. In addition, of drugs approved for orphan indications during that period, almost 50% were based on academic discoveries. So academic research is an important engine for innovation in drug discovery. Nevertheless, as Begley and Ellis conclude, the bar for reproducibility in performing and presenting preclinical studies must be raised. More rigorous preclinical research in academia will reduce waste of research and money in industry, thus leading to a cheaper drug discovery effort and a benefit to patients.

Box 2.5: The Bottom Line

The bar for reproducibility in performing and presenting preclinical studies carried out by academic scientists must be raised, lest innovative academic work go unnoticed by industry partners.

2.2 Repurposing Drugs

Kevin Grimes

Drug repurposing (also called drug repositioning) refers to the practice of developing an existing drug for a new clinical indication. Typically, a drug selected for repurposing has been tested extensively in humans and has a known safety profile. The drug may have received regulatory approval for its original indication or may have stalled in development, perhaps for lack of efficacy or an unacceptable toxicity profile for a nonserious clinical indication.

Repurposing can be a faster, less risky, and more cost-effective route to benefit patients and is therefore particularly attractive for academics and other not-for-profit drug developers. Pharmaceutical companies, biotechnology companies, and health care investors are often less enthusiastic about supporting the development of a repurposed drug because the active compound is typically not patentable. Nonetheless, proprietary claims regarding formulation, dosing, or clinical indication may allow a period of exclusive marketing and lead to a profitable program. The repurposing of the teratogenic sedative thalidomide for the treatment of multiple myeloma is an example of the profitable exploitation of a drug whose patent had long ago expired.

While physicians often prescribe drugs for "off label" uses when caring for individual patients, a drug repurposing development program for a novel indication will require clinical human experimentation and, therefore, approval of your Institutional Review Board (IRB). Advancing a repurposed compound to clinical study may also require the filing of an Investigational New Drug application (IND) with the US Food and Drug Administration (FDA) or relevant national regulatory agency (if the clinical studies will be conducted outside of the USA).

Drug studies typically require a new IND if the research will be reported to the FDA in support of a marketing claim for the new indication, i.e., a new drug label, or if the research involves a "route of administration or dosage level or use in a patient population or other factor *that significantly increases the risks* (or decreases the acceptability of the risks) associated with the use of the drug product" [7]. When in doubt, check with your institution's legal or compliance office or directly with the FDA.

Box 2.6: Key Terms and Abbreviations

Repurposing: finding a new indication, formulation or route of administration for an existing drug
Off-label: indications not listed on the drug label (and therefore not evaluated by the FDA)
IRB (Institutional Review Board): a committee formally designated by an institution to review, approve the initiation of, and conduct periodic reviews of biomedical research involving human subjects
IND: Investigational New Drug application; document filed with the FDA prior to initiating research on human subjects using any drug that has not been previously approved for the proposed clinical indication, dosing regimen, or patient population
FDA: Food and Drug Administration
NIH: National Institutes of Health
Drug Master File: a confidential document submitted to the FDA (or national regulatory agency) outlining specifications for the manufacturing, processing, packaging and storing of a therapeutic agent(s)
GLP: Good Laboratory Practice; extensive documentation of each procedural step to ensure high quality, reproducible studies
Pharmacokinetics: measurements of what the body does to a drug (absorption, distribution, metabolism and excretion)

2.2.1 *Identifying Repurposing Opportunities*

When we have discovered a novel, validated drug target, screening a library of previously approved drugs for activity against our target may lead to a drug repurposing opportunity. Researchers at the US National Institutes of Health

(NIH) have assembled a comprehensive list of drugs that have been previously approved by the FDA ($n = 2{,}356$) and by regulatory agencies worldwide ($n = 3{,}936$, inclusive of the FDA). In addition, they have compiled a library of 2,750 of these previously approved drugs and of 4,881 drugs that have undergone human testing, but have not been granted regulatory approval [8]. Researchers may apply to have the NIH test their targets against this library. Alternatively, many high-throughput screening (HTS) centers now also include a collection of previously approved drugs as a part of their chemical library.

A second path to repurposing is to apply a known modulator of a specific biologic target to a new disease. For example, eflornithine is an inhibitor of ornithine decarboxylase (ODC), a key enzyme in mammalian cells for converting ornithine to polyamines. The polyamines, in turn, are important in cell proliferation, differentiation and growth. Eflornithine stalled in development when it failed to show adequate efficacy as an antitumor agent, but has subsequently been successfully redirected as a treatment for African sleeping sickness, since ODC is also present in the causative parasite.

A third avenue for identifying repurposing opportunities is through astute clinical observation and exploitation of known or unanticipated side effects. For example, erythromycin is well known for causing gastrointestinal distress and diarrhea. This observation had led to its clinical use as a promotility agent in selected patients with a functional, non-obstructive ileus. Similarly, sildenafil originally entered clinical development as an anti-angina/antihypertensive agent. A serendipitous clinical observation led to its development as a treatment for erectile dysfunction—an extremely lucrative market opportunity.

The following sections will discuss the repurposing of drugs based upon the drug's regulatory status, patent status, and intended indication, dose, and route of indication. In general, the regulatory agencies will focus first and foremost on the safety of the proposed dosage and formulation in the new patient population. Of course, we must also show efficacy to gain regulatory marketing approval.

2.2.2 Previously Approved Drugs Using the Same (or Lower) Dose and Route of Administration

This category presents the fastest route to the clinic. If the drug is generically available and the intended patient population is not at increased safety risk, there are relatively few barriers to conducting a clinical study and publishing the results. Of course, we will require IRB approval prior to initiating the study. Once we publish our study results, physicians will be free to prescribe the drug off-label without a formal regulatory approval for the new indication. If there is reason to suspect increased risk or that the known drug risks are less acceptable for the intended indication and study population, we must file an IND.

If the drug is proprietary, we should consider approaching the company that markets the drug to solicit support for our study. Depending upon the size of the current market and the number of years remaining on the patents, the company may see our repurposing proposal as either an opportunity or a threat. Our proposed new market may represent an attractive pipeline extension. On the other hand, unanticipated negative adverse effects in the clinical study may threaten the existing franchise. If an IND is required, we must have the company's approval for the FDA to access their proprietary Drug Master File at the agency; thus, company consent is required. If an IND is not required, we may proceed with our study, even without the company's consent, assuming that we have obtained IRB approval and have adequate financial resources.

Working with the company can provide many advantages beyond financial support or free study drug. The company scientists will have an extensive working knowledge of the drug's metabolism, formulation, side effects, and potential drug–drug interactions. This information can be invaluable in the design and execution of the new clinical study.

2.2.3 New Route of Administration, Dosing, or Formulation

Regulatory agencies require that a drug be both safe and efficacious. When a drug is administered via a different route (e.g., via inhalation instead of intravenously), at higher dosages, or in a new formulation, the safety profile will be altered and human efficacy will be unproven. Therefore, an IND will be required.

Although prior human experience with the drug can be predictive and help guide preclinical studies, supplemental GLP safety studies will typically be required to determine that the route, dose, or formulation is safe to test in humans. At a minimum, preclinical studies should be conducted to assess safety and characterize pharmacokinetics for the new formulation and/or route of administration. Non-GLP preclinical efficacy studies can be useful in demonstrating biological effect and predicting the clinical dosing requirements. An open discussion with the regulatory agency early in the course of development can be invaluable in determining which preclinical studies will be required prior to entering clinical study.

2.2.4 Non-approved Drug with Human Trial Data

A number of drugs fail to advance beyond their initial phase 2 or 3 clinical study because of lack of efficacy for their intended clinical indication. These drugs are typically "shelved" by the sponsoring company, but can be very valuable if a new target or clinical indication can be identified. The timeline for developing a "shelved" drug for a new indication can be appreciably shortened and less costly because the company sponsor already has a complete preclinical package, human safety data, and a Drug Master File with the FDA (or similar regulatory agency). Often, clinical grade drug product is also available if it still meets its quality specifications. Typically, we must work with the original company sponsor because the drug is under patent protection and/or all the previous data filed with the regulatory agency is proprietary and owned by the company. The US NIH has recently announced an industry/government collaboration program that provides access to academicians to test such compounds [9].

Box 2.7: The Bottom Line

Drug repositioning can be a faster, less risky, and less expensive route to develop a new therapy for a clinical indication. Repurposing is particularly attractive for academics and other not-for-profit drug developers who are seeking cures for patients, but have limited financial resources. Some repurposing programs can be quite successful commercially if they have intellectual property claims that block competitors or privileged regulatory status (e.g., orphan disease designation).

2.3 Developing Assays for High-Throughput Screening (HTS)

Bruce Koch

The aim of HTS of chemical libraries is to identify small molecules (chemical leads) that *hit* or affect a protein target or cellular phenotype. The screen typically identifies good starting chemical entities that will be improved upon (optimized) using medicinal chemistry. There are alternative approaches for identifying small libraries of chemical leads, such as searching the published literature (including patents) or screening substrate or transition state analogs. *In silico* and fragment-based screening are also options for screening large libraries of molecules, but these methods require prior target structure elucidation and high assay sensitivity, in the case of fragment-based screening. Here we focus on the development of assays for identifying and characterizing active compounds from large (>100,000 compounds) drug-like molecule libraries using HTS.

What is unique about HTS? It relies on robust, miniaturized, "mix and measure" assays. A robust assay is one with a high Z'-factor [10], good reproducibility between runs, and resistance to interference. With the large compound libraries typically screened via HTS, cost and logistics often dictate that only a single well per compound be run. Thus, even with a high Z'-factor, there are considerable opportunities for false positive (non-reproducible) and false negative (missed actives) results due to random variation. This should be considered when designing, optimizing, and characterizing the primary screening assay. Often, multiple iterations of assay design and testing are required to adapt a low-throughput (<50 samples) assay for optimal performance in HTS.

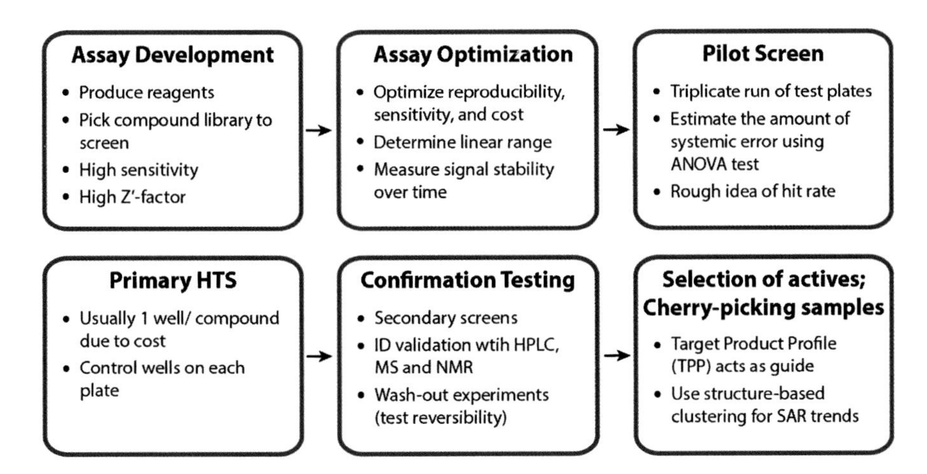

Fig. 2.1 General high-throughput screen workflow

The typical HTS workflow can be broken into the following steps (Fig. 2.1):

1. Procuring or scaling up production of the reagents (e.g., proteins or cells, substrates, solvents, reporters)
2. Developing the assay, including miniaturization
3. Assay optimization (e.g., Z'-factor, reproducibility, sensitivity)
4. Characterization of the optimized assay (e.g., sensitivity to time and temperature, linear range)
5. Pilot screen with triplicate runs of a small selection of the compound library
6. Primary HTS
7. Selection of actives and cherry-picking samples
8. Confirmation testing
9. Compound structure-based clustering
10. Confirmation of hits, evaluating the purity and identity of selected actives using LC-MS followed by NMR, and confirming activity in secondary assays

HTS assays are typically run in 2–30 μl in 384 or 1,536 well microtiter plates, although some assays resist miniaturization beyond 96 well plates. The choice of assay technology is often dependent upon the detection equipment available, cost of reagents (particularly for a screen of a large library of compounds), stability of the reagents, ease of use, and the potential for assay technology-dependent false positives.

Box 2.8: Key Terms and Abbreviations

Chemical hit: small molecule that affected the target or phenotype
HTS: high-throughput screening
Optimization: medicinal chemistry effort to improve the properties of a chemical lead

(continued)

Box 2.8 (continued)

Mix and measure assay: an assay that does not require washing away any of its components
Z'-factor: measure of assay signal relative to noise
Competitive inhibitor: molecule that binds to the target enzyme and excludes substrate binding (and vice versa)
Uncompetitive inhibitor: molecule that binds only to the target enzyme-substrate complex
Noncompetitive inhibitor: molecule that binds to the target enzyme independent of substrate binding
Edge-effect: situation in which outside wells of a multi-well plate have a bias toward different values than the rest of the plate
K_m (Michaelis constant): substrate concentration at which an enzymatic reaction rate is ½ of the maximal reaction rate. K_m is a way to characterize the enzyme's affinity for the substrate.

Once an assay technology is chosen, assay design and optimization involves tradeoffs between assay sensitivity to compounds, Z'-factor, and cost. If cost is not a consideration, one can often add large amounts of detection reagent and get both an enhanced Z'-factor and an increased sensitivity to inhibition by compound. In practice, especially for an academic effort, cost is an important consideration. For enzyme assays, the choice of substrate concentration (relative to K_m) will affect the type of inhibitors or activators that are identified. Running the assay with the starting substrate concentration equal to K_m will give the best overall sensitivity to competitive, uncompetitive, and noncompetitive inhibitors [11]. Unlike most assays designed to study enzyme kinetics, HTS assays often allow substrate conversion to proceed to around 50%, since this produces much better signal/noise at a loss of only ~1.4-fold in sensitivity to competitive compound inhibition [12]. Phenotypic screens use a biological response (e.g., cell death, protein translocation) to report compound activity. Because phenotypic responses reflect a complex biological cascade, they can be more accurate readouts of the therapeutic potential of a molecule. Confirmation via secondary assays, however, can be more difficult, as the compound target in a phenotypic screen may be unknown.

Box 2.9: Z'-Factor Defined

The Z'-factor reports the statistical effect size of the difference between an assay's signal (positive control) and noise (negative control). Good HTS assays have a Z'-factor between 0.5 and 1.

$$Z'\text{-factor} = 1 - \frac{3(\sigma_p + \sigma_n)}{|\mu_p - \mu_n|}$$

Where data follows a normal distribution and:

(continued)

Box 2.9 (continued)

σ_p: standard deviation of positive control replicates
σ_n: standard deviation of negative control replicates
μ_p: mean of the positive control replicates
μ_n: mean of the negative control replicates

Once the assay has been developed, it often will require optimization to obtain an adequately high Z'-factor and robustness. This is particularly true if the assay suffers from "edge-effects," a situation where the outside wells (in a control plate) have a bias toward different values than the rest of the plate. This can be caused by differences in temperature (plates warm up from the outside), evaporation, and in the case of plated cell-based assays, differential cell growth. It can take considerable experimental effort to identify the cause(s) of the artifact and redesign the assay to minimize its effects. As an example, for a thermal gradient edge effect, a long incubation with a lower enzyme concentration might replace a short incubation to allow time for thermal equilibration before assay readout.

Box 2.10: What Surprised an Academician?

Nearly all high-throughput screens identify reproducible (i.e., not produced by variance) false positives. This is why it is so important to have secondary assays with different reporters to confirm hits.

During assay optimization, the assay conditions should be characterized with regard to linearity with the concentration of the target protein (e.g., binding and enzyme assays), linearity with time, stability of the reagents on the assay equipment (necessary because of the time required for assay runs), solvent (typically DMSO), sensitivity, and pharmacology (if suitable standards are available). If it doesn't interfere with the assay, it is advisable to use fairly high concentrations (5–10% v/v) of DMSO, since this tends to increase the solubility of many compounds. However, cell-based assays are typically relatively sensitive to DMSO, with the limit often being at 0.5–2% v/v.

After assay optimization, the assay protocol is "frozen" and a pilot screen is run to rigorously test whether the assay is ready for HTS. Three identical sets of compound plates (typically several thousand unique compounds) are run through the assay, one set (in randomized plate order) per run. The data are analyzed using analysis of variance to determine the sizes of the systematic errors due to plate order, plate row, plate column, etc. Ideally the variance is almost all "random," with only very small contributions from systematic errors.

All HTS assay designs result in the identification of reproducible (i.e., not produced by variance) false positives. These can result from compound interference with the assay readout or from undesirable modes of interaction with the target.

Examples include reactivity of the test compound leading to covalent modification of the target, or compounds that inhibit the detection of a reporter gene directly; a common concern in a luciferase-based assay. Thus, it is essential to develop additional independent assays to validate the *hits* (active compounds) from the primary screen or, if that is not possible, to eliminate potential mechanisms producing false positives.

These validation assays should seek to answer the following questions:

1. Does the compound interact directly and reversibly with the molecular target, and with reasonable stoichiometry?
2. Does the reported structure of the active compound match what is in the well? Is it reasonably (>90%) pure? If the compound is <99% pure, is the activity quantitatively the same after purification or resynthesis?
3. Does the compound interfere directly with the reporter readout used?
4. Is compound activity quantitatively reproducible using a different assay technology (e.g., cell-based versus *in vitro*)?
5. Is the activity reversible after washout? (The relationship between potency and expected off-rate should be considered.)
6. Is there evidence of a structure–activity relationship (SAR) for the active compounds? Are there related inactive compounds in the library?
7. Is the compound just generally reactive under the assay conditions? This can be assessed by comparing compound activity before and after incubation with potential target moieties (e.g., 5 mM lysine dissolved in assay buffer).

Following these steps should result in a well-characterized primary screening assay and a set of secondary assays suitable for a HTS campaign in academia or one of the NIH Molecular Libraries Probe Production Centers Network.

Box 2.11: Recommendations

For a biochemical HTS assay, substrate concentration should be equal to K_m to help identify competitive, uncompetitive, and noncompetitive inhibitors. Different conditions may be required to identify activators (depending on the sensitivity of the assay). Usually 50% of the substrate should be converted to product for optimal signal/noise.

For cell-based assays, the percentage of organic solvents should be minimized and solvent-alone should be run as a control during assay development. Live cell imaging can be particularly challenging for large libraries unless the microscope is also in a temperature, % CO_2, and humidity-controlled environment.

Box 2.12: Key Web Sites

NIH Molecular Libraries Program
http://commonfund.nih.gov/molecularlibraries/overview.aspx
Lilly/NCGC Assay Guidance Manual
http://www.ncgc.nih.gov/guidance/manual_toc.html
Society for Laboratory Automation and Screening
http://www.slas.org/
Journal of Biomolecular Screening
http://jbx.sagepub.com/

2.4 Medicinal Chemistry and Lead Optimization

Daniel A. Erlanson

Lead optimization means taking a small molecule with promising properties and transforming this "hit" into a drug. It is like molecular sculpture, but instead of developing an aesthetically pleasing statue (which sometimes occurs), the aim is to construct a safe and effective molecule for treating a specific disease. And instead of chisels and plaster, practitioners—medicinal chemists—apply the tools of chemical synthesis.

The previous section covered HTS which, if successful, has generated a hit, a small molecule that has some activity for the target or phenotype of interest. Of course, this hit is likely a long way from being a drug. Improving affinity is often the first task of lead optimization. A drug should be as potent as possible to reduce the cost of production, to minimize the size of the pill or injection needed, and to reduce the potential for off-target effects. Most drugs have IC_{50} or EC_{50} values (half maximal inhibitory concentration or half maximal effective concentration) around 10 nM or so, with considerable variation to either side. Hits from HTS are sometimes nanomolar potency, but more often low micromolar, which means that binding affinity may need to be improved by several orders of magnitude.

2.4.1 Lead Optimization Considerations

2.4.1.1 Improved Affinity

Knowing how the molecule binds can generate ideas on how to improve potency. For example, there may be a pocket on the protein near the small molecule, and adding a chemical group (or moiety) to reach this pocket may pick up additional interactions and thus additional binding energy. Alternatively, a structure may reveal an unfavorable contact: perhaps a hydrophobic (water-hating) portion of the ligand is exposed to solvent, or a hydrophilic (water-loving) portion is buried in a greasy hydrophobic part of the protein; the medicinal chemist would make analogs of the molecule without the unfavorable contact and test the activities of the new molecules. Ideally this will lead to better potency, but often changes are less dramatic than expected, and additional molecules will need to be made. This iterative process is called structure-based drug design. In the best cases, it is possible to obtain structural information of how the small molecule binds to the target using experimental techniques such as X-ray crystallography or NMR spectrometry. Failing this, computational modeling can give some idea of the binding mode if the structure of the target is known or is believed to be similar to another characterized target.

It is also possible to do lead optimization in the absence of structure by making somewhat random changes to the molecule and seeing what effects these have on activity. Over the course of several iterations, structure-activity relationships (SARs) emerge. SAR can provide a wealth of knowledge that a medicinal chemist can use to understand the binding mode. Although experimental structural information has become a key tool in medicinal chemistry, it is worth remembering that X-ray crystallography was not sufficiently rapid and general for routine use until the 1980s and 1990s, and even today medicinal chemistry is applied to many targets for which direct structural information is not available, such as most membrane proteins.

Box 2.13: Key Terms and Abbreviations

HTS: high-throughput screening
IC_{50}: half maximal inhibitory concentration
EC_{50}: half maximal effective concentration
Chemical moiety: a functional group or portion of a molecule
SAR: structure–activity relationships
Lipophilicity: the tendency of a molecule to partition between oil and water
PK: pharmacokinetics
ADME: absorption, distribution, metabolism and excretion
PD: pharmacodynamics
hERG channel: human Ether-à-go-go-Related Gene channel, a potassium ion channel that is important to normal electrical activity of the heart. Inhibition of this channel can lead to sometimes fatal cardiac arrhythmias
CYP: cytochrome P450; a large and diverse group of enzymes that play a major role in drug metabolism

2.4.1.2 Improved Selectivity

Selectivity is another critical factor in lead optimization. Researchers generally want their drug lead to be active against the target of interest but not active against other proteins. Selectivity is most readily assessed by simply measuring activity of the molecule against other proteins, especially closely related ones, but this can be a daunting task. For example, there are about 500 protein kinases in the human genome, so measuring activity against all or even most of them can get pricey. Fortunately, enough companies have been working in the kinase field that there are now commercial offerings to confirm selectivity against a large number of kinases in a short period of time. However, such selectivity testing for newer classes of targets and enzymes is often not available. Note that selectivity testing within a related family of enzymes or receptors does not rule out the possibility that your compound will bind to a protein outside that family. Before compounds advance into the clinic they are tested against a panel of up to several hundred targets that could cause problems (see below). However, not everything can be tested *in vitro*, and off-target effects often manifest as side effects and toxicity during *in vivo* studies.

2.4.1.3 Improved Physicochemical Properties

Throughout the course of lead optimization, it is important to keep an eye on the physicochemical properties of the molecule such as solubility and lipophilicity (the way it partitions between water and oil or membranes). Solubility, in particular, can be a tricky balancing act because improving potency often involves increasing the size and lipophilicity of a molecule, leading to decreased solubility. Chemists sometimes refer to particularly insoluble compounds as "brick dust."

2.4.1.4 Improved Biological Potency

Initial screens are often conducted using pure isolated proteins under highly artificial conditions. Therefore, it is essential that potency be determined in more biologically relevant systems such as whole cell assays; all too often compounds that show activity against the isolated protein will show less or no activity in cells. Sometimes this is due to factors that a medicinal chemist may be able to fix rationally. For example, compounds that are negatively charged can have difficulty crossing cell membranes to interact with targets inside the cell. In other cases, it is unclear why there is a disconnect; in these cases it may be necessary to make more dramatic changes to the lead series, or switch to another series entirely.

2.4.1.5 Improved Pharmacological Properties

Potency and selectivity are important, but other parameters also require optimization. In fact, a rookie mistake is to focus exclusively on potency. Many things can happen to a drug on its way to its target. This is especially true for oral drugs: the body treats anything coming in through the mouth as food and tries to digest it or, failing that, to excrete it. The study of what happens to a drug *in vivo* is called pharmacokinetics (PK), which is covered in more detail in Sect. 2.8. A critical aspect of lead optimization is to measure and improve the ADME (absorption, distribution, metabolism and excretion) properties of a molecule, keeping it in the body for long enough and at sufficient levels to do its job without causing problems. Many of the individual proteins that affect a drug's path into and through the body are known, and experiments with isolated enzymes, plasma, or liver extracts can be helpful, but ultimately animal studies are essential to understand a molecule's PK.

Because so many different factors are at play in pharmacokinetics, medicinal chemists often turn to empirically derived rules to try to tune the properties of their molecules. The most famous of these is Chris Lipinski's Rule of 5, a set of guidelines concerning molecular weight, lipophilicity, and other properties that predict the likelihood a drug candidate will be orally bioavailable [13]. When performing SAR to optimize PK, often a specific moiety may be prone to metabolism, and by altering this bit of the small molecule the overall stability can be improved. Keep in mind that such rules are not hard cut-offs, but directional guidelines to improve the probability of success.

2.4.1.6 Target Validation

Pharmacokinetics is sometimes characterized as "what your body does to a drug." Conversely, pharmacodynamics (PD) can be thought of as "what a drug does to your body." On a fundamental level, the drug needs to be active against the target of interest.

Unfortunately, it is possible to inhibit or activate a biological target and yet have no effect on the disease of interest—this is particularly true for newer targets. Validated targets are targets for which modulation of their activity alters a disease state, and the best way to validate a target is through the use of a small molecule (or peptide or protein). A tool compound can be used for target validation; this is a molecule that has sufficient activity and ADME properties to answer basic biological questions about the target, but may not be suitable as a drug, perhaps because it is toxic or has other deleterious properties.

Box 2.14: What Surprised an Academician?

We started KAI with three drug candidates for three different clinical indications. When asked by the VC to rename them (to differentiate them from those used in my academic laboratory), I thought it was silly that they did not accept the names KAI 001, KAI 002 and KAI 003. In my naiveté, I was sure that we would not need to make more than 999 compounds after all the preliminary work in my university lab. I also did not realize that a company should not reveal to others how many compounds were made (e.g., if few were made, the IP might not be that strong). So instead of giving sequential numbers, our VC dubbed KAI-9803 based on my answers to "what year did you design that peptide?" and "where did it fall in the sequence of peptides you designed that year?".
–DM-R

2.4.1.7 Reduced Toxicity and Drug–Drug Interactions

There is a growing consensus that virtually all drugs have off-target effects, and it is important to understand these and determine whether they will cause adverse events. Toxicology is concerned with specific toxic effects, for example liver damage. A number of molecular substructures are known to have caused toxicity in the past, and medicinal chemists try to avoid having these moieties in their lead molecules. Ultimately though, it is impossible to predict whether a given molecule will be nontoxic without doing *in vivo* experiments.

Moreover, toxicity is not the only problem; there are many other "anti-targets" that a drug lead should avoid hitting. One of the most important is a cardiac ion channel protein called hERG, which when inhibited can cause severe and sometimes fatal heart problems. This has led to the withdrawal of several marketed drugs, and medicinal chemists today almost universally assess the hERG activity of their leads. The SAR of hERG binding is partially understood, and often medicinal chemists can engineer promising leads to maintain potency against the target protein and also avoid hitting hERG.

Similarly, many of the enzymes involved in metabolizing drugs (particularly a large class of enzymes called CYPs) can also be inhibited by small molecules, which can lead to drug–drug interactions if the enzymes in question are necessary for metabolizing other drugs. During the course of lead discovery it is important to measure CYP inhibition and, ideally, to make changes to the molecule to reduce or eliminate it.

Pharmacokinetics and pharmacology are both utterly dependent on animal models, but it is important to always remember that mice are not furry little people: drugs metabolized rapidly in mice may be stable in humans and vice versa. Because of such differences, obtaining animal data in at least two different species is usually necessary before moving a drug into the clinic.

2.4.2 Other Issues

A recent trend in medicinal chemistry is fragment-based drug discovery. Instead of starting with low micromolar IC_{50} lead-sized or drug-sized molecules, this approach starts with smaller "fragments" with molecular weights one-quarter to one-half the size of typical drugs and potencies in the mid to high micromolar range. Because there are fewer small fragments than larger molecules (just as there are fewer two letter words than four letter words), it is possible to more efficiently screen chemical diversity. Moreover, smaller, simpler molecules are less likely to have extraneous bits that do not help the overall potency but cause problems with PK or PD. Of course, identifying and optimizing lower affinity molecules are challenges in their own right.

Box 2.15: The Bottom Line

Multi-parameter molecule optimization in the absence of complete data is what makes medicinal chemistry as much an art as a science. The fact that an acceptable solution may not exist can makes it a particularly frustrating art.

Ultimately lead optimization requires the medicinal chemist to improve numerous parameters simultaneously: potency, selectivity, solubility, PK and PD. Unfortunately improving one may exacerbate another. Medicinal chemistry requires picking the best possibilities to explore, even though it is impossible to gather all data for every compound.

In fact, there is no guarantee that it is even *possible* to produce a molecule that satisfies all the necessary parameters; targets for which this is the case are called "undruggable." This multi-parameter optimization in the absence of complete data is what makes medicinal chemistry as much an art as a science, and the fact that a solution may not exist sometimes makes it a particularly frustrating art. The next time you take a drug, it is worth reflecting on the effort, skill, and serendipity that went into discovering that little molecular sculpture.

Box 2.16: Resources

1. *Journal of Medicinal Chemistry* (http://pubs.acs.org/journal/jmcmar)
This is probably the premier journal for medicinal chemistry but has onerous requirements for compound characterization.
2. *Bioorganic and Medicinal Chemistry Letters* (http://www.sciencedirect.com/science/journal/0960894X).
Because medicinal chemistry papers are often not submitted for publication until years after the work has been completed, some compounds may be missing key data, and so many researchers, particularly in industry, publish in this journal. It has a lower bar to publication, but some excellent work appears here too.
3. *In the Pipeline*
(http://www.corante.com/pipeline/)
This is probably the best chemistry-related blog out there. The author, Derek Lowe, is an experienced medicinal chemist who writes prolifically about a range of topics, and his posts attract dozens of comments.
4. *Practical Fragments* (http://practicalfragments.blogspot.com/)
For all things having to do with fragment-based drug discovery and early stage lead optimization, my blog is a good resource.

2.5 Vaccine Development

Harry Greenberg

Few if any biomedical interventions have been as successful at preventing morbidity and mortality as vaccines. The eradication of smallpox, the near eradication of paralytic polio and the potential reduction of the global burden of hepatocellular and cervical cancer are just a few of the many benefits that have been rendered by vaccines in the last 50 years. Along with their great impact, in many ways vaccines are one of the most egalitarian of all health interventions, since their benefits generally are well suited for delivery to both wealthy and poor countries alike. Therefore, vaccines have the ability to rapidly and efficiently alter the face of global health and well being.

Vaccines are molecular moieties (or antigens) that are administered to people via a number of routes, such as parenterally (e.g., intramuscular, subcutaneous, intradermal) or via a mucosal surface (e.g., orally or intranasally). In general, they are administered on only one or a few occasions because they are designed to work indirectly by eliciting a long lasting immune response in the host. They can be formulated of simple proteins or peptides, polysaccharides, nucleic acids, or complex mixtures of these constituents. In addition, vaccines can be created using complex infectious agents that are attenuated in some fashion and whose replication is restricted. These infectious agents can, on occasion, also be used to carry and express exogenous proteins.

To date, the most successful vaccines have been live attenuated infectious agents, inactivated infectious agents, or complex components of infectious agents or polysaccharides conjugated to protein carriers. Vaccines are employed to induce a host immune response that is either protective or therapeutic. Thus far, vaccines have been more effective as preventative, to avoid contracting the disease, than as therapeutic, after you have the disease, interventions. The general or even specific applicability of the "therapeutic vaccination" concept remains to be determined in humans.

Vaccination has been most successfully employed to prevent a wide variety of infectious diseases caused by many different viruses and bacteria. Vaccination against parasitic diseases has been much less successful. "Vaccination" has also been used with more limited success for treatment of allergy. In addition, a variety of experimental vaccines for the treatment of substance addiction, for birth control, and for treatment of autoimmune diseases have been studied but have not yet been widely successful. The remainder of this brief summary will therefore focus specifically on preventative vaccines against infectious diseases.

Box 2.17: Key Terms and Abbreviations

Antigen: entity that activates an immune response
Parenteral: routes for drug absorption outside the gastrointestinal tract
HIV: human immunodeficiency virus
CMV: cytomegalovirus
RSV: respiratory syncitial virus
HCV: hepatitis C virus
HA: hemagglutinin antigen
Adjuvant: compound that increases the host immune response to an antigen

2.5.1 Vaccine Efficacy

The past 50 years have witnessed the development of many highly successful new vaccines. The remaining important infectious disease targets, such as HIV, tuberculosis, malaria, CMV and RSV have remained much more difficult to prevent. Vaccine development has the highest likelihood of success when the natural infection induces a strong and enduring immunity to subsequent infection or illness. This was, for example, the case for smallpox, measles and hepatitis A and B. In other cases where reinfection can occur (usually at a mucosal surface) but secondary infection is not as often associated with severe sequelae, vaccination approaches have also been successful. This is the case with rotavirus and influenza vaccines.

When one or a few natural infections do not lead to the development of significant immunity—as is the case for HIV, HCV, gonorrhea, rhinovirus infection and malaria, for example—then it is likely that the pathway to an effective vaccine will be far more difficult. In these cases, it is likely that identification of novel immunization strategies will be required in order to develop a successful vaccine.

Two key elements in vaccine development are the availability of a predictive functional assay to measure vaccine response and a relevant animal model in which to test various immunization strategies. Animal models that replicate actual wild type infections of the microbial pathogen in the human host are most likely to be relevant. The duration, specificity and strength of the host response, as measured by a validated functional assay, are key determinants of the efficacy of the vaccine.

Box 2.18: What Surprised an Academician?

Unless the targeted disease is quite prevalent, a large number of patients must be included in vaccine trials to demonstrate efficacy—even for a highly effective vaccine. This can greatly add to development costs and duration.

2.5.2 How Vaccines Generally Work

Vaccines are designed to induce the host to mount an immune response that prevents or eliminates infection by the targeted pathogen. The induction of host immunity involves a variety of factors including many aspects of the innate immune system, the site of immune induction, the nature of the antigen, and the quantity and duration of antigen exposure. Each of these aspects needs to be carefully considered to maximize the chances of eliciting an acquired antigen-specific immune response that has functional therapeutic activity.

Whereas both T and B cell responses are often induced by vaccination, as a generality, most existing successful vaccines "work" at the effector level on the basis of the B cell and antibody responses induced. Many methods have been and are being examined to enhance the immune response to vaccines, including using an adjuvant to boost the innate immune response, using protein carriers to induce immune memory to polysaccharide antigens, and using replicating vaccines to produce more antigens with greater diversity at the site of infection. As mentioned above, when natural infection induces protective immunity, it has been relatively straightforward to design a vaccine that mimics the effective component(s) of that infection. When natural infection is not a very effective inducer of protective immunity, vaccine development has been much more difficult.

2.5.3 Some New Technologies in Vaccine Development

This short review cannot cover all the new technologies that are currently being explored to develop novel or improved vaccines. A few examples are provided to invite the reader to examine the field more extensively. Many pathogens avoid host immunity by altering or expanding their antigenic diversity. Examples include such diverse organisms as influenza, HIV and pneumococcus. Recent advances in immunology have demonstrated the existence of "common" or "shared" antigens on several pathogens, such as the finding that the influenza HA stalk is a target of a protective antibody. Such targets could provide an "Achilles' Heel" to which the host can target its immune response and thereby circumvent the problem of pathogen antigenic diversity. Currently many investigators are working to design new vaccines directed at such shared antigens of influenza, HIV and pneumococcus, for example.

As an alternate approach, directed regulation of the innate immune response holds the promise of greatly enhancing the level and duration of acquired immunity following vaccination. Many investigators are now exploring the safety and efficacy of new adjuvants that directly target specific signaling molecules, thereby enhancing the innate immune response.

Finally, immunization using nucleic acids (either DNA or RNA) encoding antigenic proteins holds promise to greatly simplify vaccine manufacturing, while substantially reducing cost and enhancing safety. To date, such strategies have been highly promising in small animal models but less so in people. Continued innovation in this area, if successful, could greatly facilitate vaccine development.

2.5.4 Special Considerations Concerning Safety and Cost

There are a variety of factors that distinguish vaccine development from virtually all other areas of therapeutics development. Of course, like all other medical interventions, vaccines must be shown to be efficacious. However, unlike most other interventions, vaccines are generally given to healthy individuals with the intent of preventing a possible illness in the future rather than treating a current problem. Because of this fact, the level of tolerance for risk associated with vaccination is very dependent on the level of perceived danger from the infection being prevented. For example, when polio epidemics were common, the public clamored for a preventative intervention. However, since polio has disappeared from the Western hemisphere, even one case of immunization-induced polio per million vaccinations represents an unacceptable risk in the USA and Europe.

This common and pervasive concern with vaccine risk is often intensified because vaccines are most frequently given to young healthy children, who can be considered most vulnerable to untoward risk. In addition, the benefits of vaccination are most easily measured at the societal rather than the individual level because the odds that any given individual will be infected are frequently quite low. This dichotomy further complicates acceptance of vaccines by the public. Because of these factors, vaccine development often requires investment in very large and extensive safety testing before registration, as well as substantial post-licensing follow-up that is both expensive and complex.

Because vaccines are given to healthy individuals, because they are generally given only a few times during the life of an individual, and because of the prolonged regulatory pathway due to safety concerns as discussed above, they have frequently been perceived as providing a poor return on investment by drug developers. This is, of course, a shame, given their immense societal impact over the years.

Box 2.19: The Bottom Line

Although only one or a few doses of a vaccine are administered, vaccines are generally administered to healthy people, most often children, who are at low risk of acquiring the disease. As a result, the safety hurdle is very high, further adding to the time and cost of vaccine development.

Finally, many of the most important remaining challenges in the area of vaccine development (HIV, tuberculosis, malaria) are diseases that generally afflict the poor, disadvantaged and less developed regions of world. This fact has likely inhibited the rate of progress for these much needed interventions. Despite these issues, recent advances in immunology, material sciences and systems biology provide exciting opportunities for the vaccine innovators of the future. During the coming decade, we are likely to see vaccination for several of these challenging diseases reduced to practice.

2.6 When to Begin Animal Studies

Daria Mochly-Rosen

We have identified a new chemical entity or a known drug that affects our validated target/pathway and have shown its efficacy in a cell-based assay. What is the next step?

Experts are divided on whether it is advisable to begin animal studies right away or whether it is better to first identify the optimal compound. By generating and testing analogs of the original "hit," it may be possible to improve potency or specificity for the target. *In vitro* studies to obtain an optimal formulation for a drug or simply better solubility can also improve the chance for success once animal studies begin. And there are other considerations, such as *in vitro* assessment of drug toxicity and metabolism, including liver enzyme assays, hERG channel effects, etc. In other words, we can easily spend a year and thousands of dollars in studies aimed at improving our initial hit.

In vitro and cell-based assays are usually cheaper and faster to run than animal studies, but they are not always predictive of the *in vivo* behavior of the molecule—which is ultimately most important for determining if our hit will make a good drug. So, how are drug development programs to decide, with their limited funds, between screening lots of analogs *in vitro* versus testing only a handful of molecules in animals? As an academician that has followed over 70 programs in SPARK, my answer to this question is simple.

2.6.1 Take a Short Cut

We should start animal studies as soon as we can. It is true that many improvements to our compound can be made, but a short *in vivo* study can be extremely valuable in helping to optimize the compound and induce greater interest from partners and investors. A great deal can be learned from an imperfect drug. We might even be lucky and find that our compound shows a therapeutic benefit and drug-like properties!

We must also recognize that failure to demonstrate efficacy at this stage is not a reason to discontinue our project. These are exploratory studies and much can still be done to improve the compound's selectivity, potency, solubility, bioavailability, safety, metabolism, route of administration and final formulation.

Box 2.20: Key Terms and Abbreviations

Alzet® pumps: miniature osmotic infusion pumps for the continuous dosing of a drug to a laboratory animal
hERG channel: human Ether-à-go-go-Related Gene channel is a potassium ion channel that is important to normal electrical activity of the heart. Inhibition of this channel can lead to sometimes fatal cardiac arrhythmias
ip: intraperitoneal; within the abdominal cavity
sc: subcutaneous; beneath the skin
SAR: structure–activity relationship

2.6.2 What Animal Model to Use?

It is best to read the literature and use an animal model that is accepted in the field for the given indication. It is inadvisable to develop a new model for this first *in vivo* trial. Better yet, we can find a collaborator that is using this animal model and have them do the study for us. It is rare that such a study will generate new intellectual property—and the collaborator can provide an independent and unbiased assessment of our compound.

2.6.3 How to Deliver the Drug?

Even if we believe that oral administration is the ideal route for our clinical indication, it is ill advised to attempt to do the first efficacy study in animals using oral gavage. Instead consider intraperitoneal (ip) injection. If the drug is not very soluble, we can deliver the drug with ethanol, DMSO or polyethylene glycol; animals will tolerate quite a high dose of these solvents. If there is concern that the drug dose will be too low using ip injection, we can consider using a subcutaneous (sc) Alzet® osmotic pump. The company's Web site details a number of sizes and recommended solvents as well as training on how to implant them—all very easy.

Box 2.21: What Surprised an Academician?

When selecting a delivery formulation for these initial animal studies, simpler is always better. We once used over the counter beauty lotion for an initial topical delivery study because it had the desired aqueous formulation properties. *–DM-R*

2.6.4 *Start with a Small Safety Study*

To make sure that the drug dose is not fatal, we can inject a couple of healthy animals and observe them for a few hours for obvious signs of toxicity. A veterinary nurse can help with monitoring for adverse events. Once we know that the dose selected is not acutely toxic, we can jump into efficacy and longer safety studies in the chosen animal model of disease.

2.6.5 *Learn as much as You Can from the First* In Vivo *Study*

Animals are precious and should be used sparingly. Therefore, we should plan experiments carefully to include proper controls. If there is a drug that is known to be efficacious in the model, we should treat three to four animals with that drug to serve as a positive control. We can include a vehicle control if we are worried about effects of the vehicle. Otherwise, for this first study, just compare drug-treated to non-treated animals. When euthanizing the animals, we should collect as many organs and bio-fluids as possible for analysis. A pathologist can advise us on how to preserve the tissues and store samples for later analysis. We should attempt to collect as much data as possible relevant to our disease and to compound safety. The bottom line: we need to maximize the information obtained from this first set of studies.

2.6.6 *If the Short-Cut Failed*

We are not done! Remember that we have committed to take the long route even if the shortcut failed. We can go back and perform further SAR studies with analogs of our hit and additional studies on drug solubility and *in vitro* toxicity. We can now focus on correcting the problems identified based upon the first *in vivo* experiment.

2.6.7 *If the Short-Cut Succeeded*

Congratulations! The work has just begun. But now we have more compelling data that the project is worth pursuing. Make sure to consult Sect. 2.1 on robust preclinical work and Sect. 2.7 on *in vivo* pharmacology to plan your next steps.

Box 2.22: The Bottom Line

An early small *in vivo* study can be extremely helpful in demonstrating both efficacy and preliminary toxicity of our drug. Results can also inform further rounds of optimization of the compound. During initial animal studies, the drug should generally be administered using a parenteral route (ip or sc via osmotic infusion pump).

2.7 *In Vivo* Pharmacology: Multiple Roles in Drug Discovery

Simeon I. Taylor

Classical drug discovery relied primarily upon testing compounds for activity in established animal models. When following this paradigm, it was not necessary to ask questions such as why one conducted *in vivo* pharmacology experiments or whether there was value in studying animal models of disease. Rather, screening in various animal models was often the first step in the drug discovery process. The use of animal models played an essential and central role in the classical drug discovery process. In the past, the molecular target was frequently unknown at the time a drug was approved for use in patients. Indeed, as illustrated by the example of sulfonylurea drugs, the molecular target (e.g., the sulfonylurea receptor) was identified several decades after the drugs were in widespread use to treat type 2 diabetes mellitus.

How times have changed! Modern drug discovery most often relies on a radically different research paradigm. Target-based drug discovery has become so entrenched that some scientists actually question whether *in vivo* experiments in animal models have any value in the modern approach to drug discovery. This section illustrates the many ways in which *in vivo* pharmacology studies in experimental animals contribute to drug discovery.

2.7.1 *Target Identification and Validation*

How are drug targets identified in the first place? While there is no simple answer to this question, proposals for new targets are often based upon genetic experiments. Genetic diseases (either in humans or in experimental animals such as mice) can generate hypotheses suggesting potential drug targets. In some cases, a gene mutation (most often a loss-of-function mutation) causes disease. For example, homozygous loss-of-function mutations in the genes encoding either leptin (*ob/ob*) or the leptin receptor (*db/db*) cause obesity in mice. Based upon the identification in 1994 of a loss-of-function mutation in the leptin gene as a cause of obesity in mice, a biotechnology company paid a large sum of money to license the relevant intellectual property from an academic institution. In other words, a biotechnology company viewed this genetic evidence as compelling validation that leptin represented a therapeutic protein to treat human obesity.

Ultimately, the clinical studies in humans were disappointing. Although leptin is efficacious in rare human diseases associated with low leptin levels (e.g., mutations in the leptin gene or lipoatrophic diabetes), it did not deliver the desired efficacy in patients with the common forms of obesity. In short, the predictive value of leptin-deficient animal models was limited to predicting the response of leptin-deficient humans to pharmacologic therapy with leptin. However, most obese patients turn out to be leptin-resistant rather than leptin-deficient. Accordingly, human responsiveness to antiobesity treatments was better predicted by a leptin resistant model (i.e., the *db*/*db* mouse with mutations in the leptin receptor gene).

Box 2.23: Why Do Some Scientists Question the Value of Studies in Animal Models?

There are many examples where data obtained from experiments in animal models fail to predict the outcome of clinical studies. It would be fallacious, however, to infer that animal studies in general are entirely without value. Animal models are idealized versions of disease where all subjects are the same age (usually young), eat the same food, and have the same routines. Human subjects are much more varied, and so will have a more variable response to treatment. This is why it is very important to know the limitations of your chosen animal model when extrapolating to expected effect in humans.

What lessons can be drawn? There are many animal models. It is essential to exercise scientific judgment before extrapolating from an animal model to human disease. For example, multiple animal models of a particular disease may yield discordant predictions. Whereas the *ob*/*ob* mouse model suggested that leptin would be a highly efficacious treatment for obesity, the *db*/*db* mouse model predicted the exact opposite. It is often necessary to carefully compare results from animal models to clinical specimens or observations to assess the predictive value of a particular animal model for a particular human disease.

There are at least three other limitations which make it difficult to extrapolate from genetic models such as knock-out mice:

- Because mutations are present at the earliest times in development, there can be important developmental effects which might not be relevant to pharmacology in adult animals. For example, if a mutation in a particular gene impacts development of an organ, this would have a profound effect upon physiology. Pharmacological inhibition of the function of the same gene product in an adult animal would not necessarily lead to the same physiological deficit.

- Many loss-of-function mutations cause disease. Accordingly, to treat the disease it may be necessary to find a drug to activate the function of the gene product. However, as illustrated by the example discussed above, leptin was not an efficacious treatment of obesity despite the fact that leptin deficiency causes obesity. In contrast, there are examples where loss-of-function mutations have been shown to promote health. For example, loss-of-function mutations in Pcsk9 lead to decreased LDL levels, thereby decreasing the risk of cardiovascular events. Subsequent data demonstrated that loss-of-function mutations in the Pcsk9 gene reliably predicted the pharmacology of Pcsk9-neutralizing antibodies.
- It seems likely that loss-of-function mutations may accurately predict the pharmacology of inhibitors or antagonists. For a variety of reasons, agonists and activators may not always exert pharmacological effects which are the opposite of the phenotype of loss-of-function mutations.

Box 2.24: Key Terms and Abbreviations

Pharmacodynamic efficacy: the ability of a compound to affect the *in vivo* activity of a target
Disease efficacy: the ability of a compound to improve the effects of disease
Off-rate: the rate of compound release after binding to the target; irreversible binders have a zero off-rate
Drug exposure: also called the AUC (Area under the curve); the integral under a plot of plasma drug concentration versus time
Pro-drug: a compound which requires metabolism after administration in order to show therapeutic activity
PK: pharmacokinetics; measurements of the absorption, distribution, metabolism and excretion of a molecule after administration
PD: pharmacodynamics; measurements of drug action in the body (e.g., target inactivation, receptor off-rate, etc.)
NOAEL: no observed adverse effect level

2.7.2 Assessing Efficacy During Lead Optimization

As a prelude to discussing the role of animal experiments in the lead optimization process, it is important to distinguish between two concepts:

- *Pharmacodynamic efficacy*. This refers to the ability of a compound to engage the molecular target *in vivo*, and also to modulate *in vivo* biology. Among other things, this requires that the compound be delivered in appropriate concentrations to the biological compartment where the target resides. It also requires that the pharmacokinetics will provide sufficient exposure of the drug to the target. There are at least two complementary approaches to assessing pharmacodynamic efficacy. (a) In some cases, it is possible to assess target occupancy (e.g., by assessing the ability of a drug to inhibit binding of PET ligands to the drug target). (b) It is often useful to assess the function of the target (e.g., by assessing the ability of a protein kinase inhibitor to decrease the phosphorylation state of a specific kinase substrate).

- *Disease efficacy*. This refers to the ability of a compound to ameliorate the manifestations of a disease. Needless to say, evidence of disease efficacy in an animal model is frequently interpreted as suggesting that the drug will also be efficacious in human disease. This expectation is not always borne out. Nevertheless, this is not a reason to entirely abandon the use of animal models simply because they are imperfect predictors of human pharmacology. Situations in which compounds show strong pharmacodynamic efficacy but lack disease efficacy can also occur, and suggest target validation was in an oversimplified model of disease.

Whether or not they turn out to predict disease efficacy in humans, animal models provide essential information for the pharmaceutical R&D process. For example, animal models can provide important insights for lead optimization:

1. Which parameters of *in vitro* pharmacology best predict disease efficacy? In many cases, the *in vitro* potency (e.g., the thermodynamic affinity with which the compound binds to its target) will be the best predictor. However, in some cases, the kinetic off-rate may be more relevant. For example, when neurotransmitters are released at synapses, this leads to very high local concentrations that persist for short durations. If a competitive antagonist has a rapid off-rate, this will allow the high concentrations of neurotransmitter to compete effectively with the drug. In contrast, if the drug has a slow off-rate, the drug will remain bound to the target during the brief time the neurotransmitter achieves its peak level. In this nonequilibrium condition, a drug with a slow off-rate will out-perform a drug with a fast off-rate even if both drugs have the identical *in vitro* potencies during equilibrium binding conditions.
2. Which parameter(s) of drug exposure best predict disease efficacy *in vivo*? In some cases, peak drug levels drive disease efficacy—e.g., for transcriptional activators that promote expression of long-lived proteins. In other cases, drug exposure (the integral of drug concentration over time) drives disease efficacy—e.g., if it is necessary to sustain inhibition of a target for 24 h a day.
3. Does the drug reach the appropriate compartment to drive disease efficacy? Sometimes, a drug can accumulate in an organ because it is tightly bound to an irrelevant protein. To derive the desired pharmacology, it is necessary to achieve sufficient levels of free drug to drive the required occupancy of the correct molecular target.
4. Do metabolites show pharmacological activity? In some cases, compounds will undergo metabolic transformation into active species. In some cases, the administered compound (i.e., the "prodrug") may be inactive and undergoes metabolic transformation into an active species. For example, prednisone is

inactive, but must be converted into the active compound, prednisolone, by 11β-hydroxysteroid dehydrogenase. In other examples, active metabolites are to blame for a compound's undesired side effects; in which case medicinal chemistry efforts will modify the lead compound to reduce that mode of metabolism. *In vivo* pharmacology experiments are essential to identify and quantitate the levels of drug metabolites and also to assess their contribution to overall pharmacology.

5. What is the projected human dose? As part of the feasibility assessment, it is necessary to estimate the expected dose required for efficacy in humans. There are at least two factors which enter into the dose projection: first, quantitation of the exposure required for efficacy in at least one animal model; and, second, prediction of the expected pharmacokinetic (PK) profile in humans. The projection of human PK is generally based upon measurement of PK in multiple species (e.g., mouse, rat, dog, and nonhuman primate).
6. How safe are the compounds and what is the therapeutic index? Safety assessment is generally conducted in two nonclinical species (one rodent and one non-rodent) prior to initiating human studies. The "no observed adverse effect level" (NOAEL) is defined as the highest exposure that can be achieved without causing adverse effects in the test species. The therapeutic index is defined as the ratio of the NOAEL exposure: efficacious exposure. To calculate the therapeutic index, it is essential to define the exposure required for efficacy in at least one animal model. This is one of the most important reasons why it is essential to have conducted efficacy studies prior to advancing a compound into development.

2.7.3 Identifying Clinical Biomarkers

Relatively long periods of treatment are often required to assess efficacy in human disease. Prior to embarking upon such studies, it is essential to define the relevant dose range to study. Toward that end, it is very useful to assess the effect of the drug on translational clinical biomarkers. For example, in the development of sodium-dependent glucose transporter-2 (SGLT2) inhibitors as antidiabetic drugs, it was possible to assess the drug's pharmacodynamics (PD) efficacy by measuring excretion of glucose in the urine. There are at least two questions which must be addressed in order to interpret clinical biomarker data:

1. Does the biomarker predict disease efficacy? In the case of SGLT2 inhibitors, loss of glucose in the urine is a direct consequence of inhibiting the transporter that mediates reabsorption of glucose from the glomerular filtrate. In addition, loss of glucose in the urine is the key mechanism that drives the decrease in plasma glucose levels. This line of reasoning provides a compelling rationale to believe that glucosuria is a valid biomarker to predict glycemic efficacy in patients with type 2 diabetes.

2. What degree of change in the biomarker is required to drive disease efficacy? By studying the biomarker in animal models of disease, it is possible to obtain experimental data to calibrate the biomarker relative to assessments of disease efficacy. There is no guarantee that the calibration derived from animal models can be extrapolated quantitatively to human disease, but it does provide a reasonable starting point. In the absence of such data from animal models, clinical investigators have no alternative but to guess at how to calibrate the biomarker.

2.7.4 Conclusion

In vivo pharmacology studies in animal models make critical contributions to many aspects of pharmaceutical R&D—including target identification, target validation, lead optimization, safety assessment, and translational biomarker identification, validation, and calibration. Unfortunately, for a variety of reasons, nonclinical studies are only imperfect predictors of clinical pharmacology. Nevertheless, perfection is seldom achieved in human endeavors. While researchers must take this limitation into account, it would be a mistake to let the perfect be the enemy of the good.

2.8 Pharmacokinetics and ADME Properties

Werner Rubas and Emily Egeler

Initial screening efforts and secondary assays to identify compounds with desired efficacy and specificity for the intended target focus on issues of pharmacodynamics (PD), which in layman's terms can be defined as "actions of a molecule (drug) on the body." For a drug to be successful, however, the active molecule must be able to reach the intended target at high enough concentrations and for a long enough time to exert its therapeutic effect. The body must also be able to remove the active molecule without significant buildup of toxic species, or the drug will fail in clinical trials. These considerations are evaluated in pharmacokinetic (PK) studies; summed up as "actions of the body on a molecule."

Pharmacokinetic studies measure the absorption, distribution, metabolism, and excretion of an administered molecule—often abbreviated as ADME characteristics.

Box 2.25: Key Terms and Abbreviations

PD: pharmacodynamics; measurements of drug action in the body (e.g., target inactivation, receptor off-rate, etc.)
PK: pharmacokinetics; measurements of the absorption, distribution, metabolism and excretion of a molecule after administration
ADME: Absorption, Distribution, Metabolism, and Excretion
CYP: Cytochrome P450, a class of enzymes important in drug metabolism
Polymorphism: genetic variation in enzymes that affects their activity and leads to differences in drug metabolism rates
iv: intravenous
po: oral
SDPK: Single dose pharmacokinetic
SAD: single ascending dose

2.8.1 Key ADME Parameters

ADME characteristics depend on both intrinsic properties of the molecule such as p*K*a, size, and lipophilicity; and extrinsic properties such as formulation or route of administration. Excellent resources exist for detailed description of the influence of each pharmacokinetic factor discussed briefly below [14].

Important ADME characteristics include those listed below and pictured in Fig. 2.2:

- Bioavailability (F)—The percentage of an administered dose that reaches the systemic circulation. Molecules administered intravenously have 100% bioavailability, whereas molecules delivered topically or orally with a high first-pass effect would have a lower bioavailability.
- Volume of distribution (V_d)—The apparent volume required to dissolve the administered dose at the drug concentration measured in the plasma. For a drug retained exclusively in the vascular compartment, the volume of distribution is equal to the plasma volume (0.04 L/kg body weight). For a drug that is extensively bound in peripheral tissues, the V_d can greatly exceed the total body volume.
- Clearance (CL)—A fraction of blood or plasma volume completely purified of drug per unit time. Total CL depends on elimination rate constant ($t_{1/2}$) and V_d. Clearance at specific organs, such as liver, kidneys, skin, lungs, etc., is dependent on the blood flow through the organ; so disease states can alter drug clearance. Intrinsic clearance (CL_{int}) refers to the measured *in vitro* clearance.
- Half-life ($t_{1/2}$)—The time required for the drug concentration to fall by 50% of an earlier measurement. Terminal half-life is calculated from the clearance and volume of distribution.

  $t_{1/2} = ((\ln 2) \times V_d)/CL$

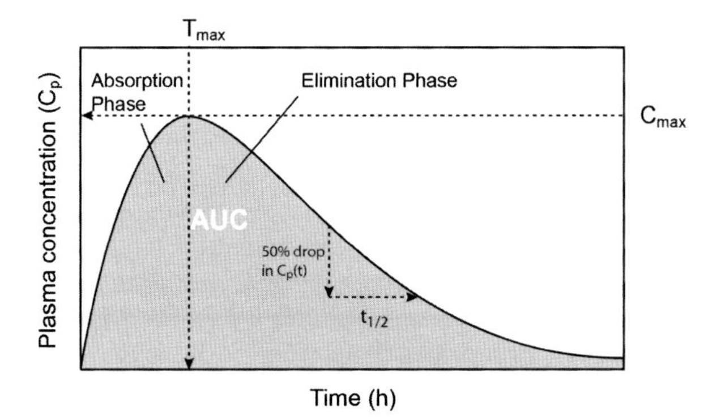

Fig. 2.2 Plasma concentration curve with PK metrics

- Area under the curve (AUC)—The integral under a plot of plasma drug concentration versus time. The AUC reflects the "total exposure" from a single dose of drug. The dose normalized ratio of $AUC_{oral}/AUC_{intravenous}$ yields bioavailability.
- First pass effect—The extent of metabolism that occurs before an orally administered drug enters the systemic circulation.

2.8.2 Drug Metabolism and Drug–Drug Interactions

The simplest form of elimination is direct excretion of an unchanged drug molecule into the urine, bile, or occasionally tears, sweat or air. More commonly, molecules undergo biotransformation, a process of metabolism that involves building or breaking chemical bonds within the molecule to improve the body's ability to excrete it. Biotransformation is grouped into Phase I and Phase II reactions; Phase I enzymes catalyze oxidations, reductions and/or hydrolysis to introduce or unmask functional groups in the molecule. Phase II enzymes conjugate endogenous small polar molecules to the unmasked functional groups to inactivate the drug and improve its water solubility for elimination. A drug may be subject to Phase I metabolism, Phase II, or both. Sometimes, knowledge of a drug's metabolism is exploited by chemists to devise a prodrug, a molecule whose metabolism creates the true therapeutically active compound, to improve ADME properties.

The cytochrome P450 (CYP) family of enzymes is composed of a number of related isozymes and is responsible for a major portion of drug Phase I metabolism. CYP enzymes are primarily located in the liver, but also occur in a number of other tissues. CYP isozymes differ in their abundance and importance to metabolism across different tissues. For instance, the CYP3A4 isoform is very abundant in the liver and intestinal epithelium and contributes to the biotransformation of almost one half of drugs, whereas CYP2D6 is one of the least abundant isozymes and yet is involved in the metabolism of a quarter of all drugs [15].

Identifying which CYP isozymes are responsible for metabolism of the lead compound, called reaction phenotyping, is important for two reasons. First, a number of genetic polymorphisms have been identified for CYP isozymes. Polymorphisms result from inherited differences in enzyme expression or mutations that alter enzyme activity. These differences create variation in the rates of drug metabolism within a patient population. Dosing regimens may need to be adjusted to properly treat slow or ultra-fast metabolizers.

The second reason for reaction phenotyping is that many drugs display off-target activity on CYP isozymes, acting as inhibitors, inducers, or both. Co-administered molecules may show altered metabolism to that of a single drug. These drug–drug interactions must be carefully screened for, as they can either negatively (creating side-effects) or positively (improving ADME properties) impact the metabolites produced.

2.8.3 In Vitro *Experiments*

Initial studies of ADME characteristics are likely to be *in vitro* due to the high cost of animal studies. Although algorithms exist to extrapolate *in vitro* data to living systems, preliminary *in vivo* studies should be performed to confirm that *in vitro* data are indeed predictive. If the results are in concurrence, a strategy of *in vitro* screening with limited *in vivo* testing can be adopted. This approach allows more rapid and cost-effective identification of compound liabilities and better selection of a formulation before moving into animal models.

A number of different test systems are available to measure the *in vitro* or intrinsic clearance (CL_{int}) and are listed in Table 2.1. CYP reaction phenotyping is typically done with panels of purified enzymes and their cofactors. Systems derived from human material are preferred for identifying drug metabolites, but other animal models are important for initial studies of drug safety. *In vitro* experiments are useful for reaction phenotyping, screening for drug–drug interactions, measuring intrinsic clearance, and identifying metabolites.

In addition, there are a number of *in vitro* models (Caco-2, MDCK, mucosal tissues and skin) to predict absorption via different routes of administration.

2.8.4 In Vivo *Experiments*

The goal of *in vivo* PK experiments is to calculate bioavailability, AUC, volume of distribution and half-life while validating the clearance and metabolite identity data collected from *in vitro* studies. The FDA requires safety studies in at least two mammalian species, including one non-rodent species. These animal studies in concert with pharmacokinetic and pharmacodynamic studies will help predict the dosing range and regimen for desired therapeutic effect and expected safe dose in humans before starting phase 1 clinical trials. Because upper dosing levels are usually set at the appearance of adverse side effects (or in the case of oncology

Table 2.1 *In vitro* test systems for intrinsic clearance

Test system	Specific models
Cell extracts	• S9 fraction (Phase I and II) • Microsomes (Phase I only)
Cell culture	• Hepatocytes (fresh or cryopreserved) • HepG2 cells transfected with CYP isozymes
Whole tissue	• Liver slices

drugs, severe adverse effects), *in vivo* pharmacokinetics studies go hand-in-hand with toxicology studies. For this reason, some people refer to *in vivo* testing as ADMET studies.

Initial *in vivo* PK studies should be done in rodents, preferably rats, in parallel with the *in vitro* testing. Dosing routes should include intravenous (IV) and the intended clinical route of administration, often oral (po). To gather as much PK data as possible, both urine and blood samples should be collected; with other fluids such as cerebrospinal fluid, perspiration, or breath collected as applicable. The second species for *in vivo* testing, often dogs or monkeys, should be chosen based on program-specific issues such as metabolite profile and pharmacology.

The first test is often a single-dose pharmacokinetic (SDPK) study to follow the ADME properties of a single bolus of administered drug. Samples are collected at many time points to create a plasma concentration curve similar to that shown in Fig. 2.2. Once the compound's ADME characteristics look promising, animal PK studies move into single ascending dose (SAD) experiments to establish the maximum acutely tolerated dose. Further studies with radiolabeled drug are used to confirm the identity of major metabolites and look at drug deposition in different tissues.

2.8.5 The Bottom Line

Pharmacokinetic studies tell researchers how the lead compound is absorbed, distributed, metabolized and excreted from the body. *In vitro* PK testing is used to identify initial metabolism rates and routes, in addition to identifying potential drug–drug interactions. *In vivo* PK testing is essential for establishing a pharmacokinetic/pharmacodynamic relationship and the maximum tolerated dose and therapeutic window in animals for a lead compound, which becomes the basis for planning safe and effective doses moving into human trials. Because different crystal forms, salts and formulations of the same compound can have different ADME characteristics, it is very important to show favorable PK properties before scaling up GMP production for clinical trials to avoid costly reformulation delays. Proper PK studies can help drug developers maximize their therapeutic window between minimum efficacious dose and maximum tolerated dose.

2.9 Route of Administration and Drug Formulation

Terrence F. Blaschke

The route of administration and the formulation of a drug are often intertwined by virtue of the chemistry and the desired onset and duration of action of the drug. The route of administration of a drug can be broadly separated into three categories: (1) Enteral, (2) Parenteral, and (3) Topical. In each of those categories, there are a number of subcategories, as follows:

1. Enteral Administration
   (a) Oral
   (b) Buccal or sublingual
   (c) Rectal
2. Parenteral Administration
   (a) Intravenous
      - Slow Bolus
      - Slow infusion, then stop
      - Continuous infusion (long-term)

   (b) Subcutaneous
      - Bolus
      - Continuous infusion (long-term, e.g., insulin)
      - Depot

   (c) Intramuscular
      - Bolus
      - Depot
3. Topical application
   (a) Transdermal (intended for systemic effects)
   (b) Epidermal/dermal (intended for local effects at site of administration)
   (c) Vaginal (usually intended for local effects)
   (d) Intranasal
   (e) Pulmonary inhalation (intended for local or systemic effects)

Each of these routes of administration requires a different type of formulation. Many companies are developing drug delivery technologies involving oral, nasal, inhalation, transdermal, and parenteral delivery platforms.

Box 2.26: Key Terms and Abbreviations

Enteral: routes for drug absorption through the gastrointestinal tract
Parenteral: routes for drug absorption outside the gastrointestinal tract
Buccal: in the mouth
Sublingual: under the tongue
Intranasal: in the nose
Bolus: a single large dose of drug
Depot: store of drug deposited in the body that is slowly released over time
Bioavailability: the fraction (or percent) of the dose of chemically unchanged drug found in the blood based on the route of administration
SR: slow release
XR: extended release
API: Active Pharmaceutical Ingredient
Bio-betters: new formulations of biologic therapeutics to improve dosing schedule or route of administration
Therapeutic index: the ratio of the toxic dose to the effective dose; a larger therapeutic index suggests a larger safety window

2.9.1 *Oral Route*

The most common, desirable, and usually the least expensive route of administration is the oral route; especially if the drug is intended for multiple doses or chronic administration. However, for many drugs, the oral route may not be feasible or practical, as the drug may show poor oral bioavailability and not reach the systemic circulation after oral dosing. For the oral route, there are many forms (tablet, capsule, liquid, suspension, etc.) chosen and manufactured on the basis of the bioavailability of the drug.

Another important characteristic of an oral formulation is its rate of absorption. In some settings, rapid absorption is desirable, to achieve a rapid onset of action (e.g., drugs given for pain or for sleep). Tablets may be formulated as "quick dissolve" versions. In other settings rapid absorption is problematic, as the high peak concentrations associated with rapid absorption may result in unwanted side effects, sometimes serious or life-threatening. There are many examples of this in the cardiovascular field.

There are a number of special formulations used for oral administration intended to prolong the duration of action and/or avoid high peak concentrations. These are often called "slow release" (SR) or "extended release" (XR) formulations, to distinguish them from immediate release formulations. Such formulations may allow a drug to be administered at longer dosing intervals that improve patient adherence to the medication (e.g., once instead of twice daily, or twice instead of three times daily). Other special oral formulations include enteric-coated formulations that protect the drug from the acidic environment of the stomach and dissolve in the intestines, or fixed-dose combinations containing two or more active pharmaceutical ingredients (APIs) that are used for conditions benefiting from combined drug therapy (e.g., hypertension, diabetes and HIV).

Box 2.27: What Frustrated an Academician?

Not all drugs reach their target when delivered in a simple formulation. Proper formulation and route of delivery is also critical when using new pharmacological agents for basic research, whether in culture or *in vivo*. It is important to include studies on drug stability and distribution for each formulation of a new pharmacological agent.

2.9.2 Parenteral Route (Injectables)

For drugs that cannot reach the systemic circulation after enteral or transdermal administration, or for drugs for which a very rapid onset of action is needed, parenteral dosage forms are required. Parenteral routes also avoid the first-pass metabolism in the liver experienced by orally administered drugs. For direct intravenous administration, the drug must be solubilized in a liquid suitable for direct injection into a vein, or—much less commonly—into an artery. Speed of injection (bolus, slow infusion or constant infusion) is dependent on the indication. For anesthetics and sedative/hypnotics used in procedures, and for some cardiac arrhythmias, slow bolus injections are often used. However, for many other agents that are not orally available (e.g., many anticancer agents and the rapidly increasing number of biologics on or close to the market) a slow infusion is preferable to avoid toxicity associated with high peak concentrations and rapid distribution into tissues where unwanted effects can occur (e.g., the central nervous system, heart or other vital organs). With the advent of reliable, miniaturized infusion pumps, there is increasing interest in research evaluating whether the therapeutic index could be improved by longer-term infusions. The subcutaneous infusion of insulin is an example of this approach to therapy of diabetes. Examples in other chronic diseases will no doubt follow.

2.9.3 Epidermal or Transdermal Route

Epidermal or transdermal formulations are generally patches or gels. If systemic absorption is the goal of transdermal delivery, there are many characteristics of the drug that may limit this route. In particular, drugs must be of high potency, be able to penetrate the epidermis, and benefit from a fairly constant concentration in the blood. Alternatively, transdermal or epidermal routes may be selected to deliver a high local concentration of drug and avoid systemic exposure. There is increasing interest in this route of administration. Patches are easy to use (improving patient adherence), provide continuous dosing of a steady drug concentration, and avoid first-pass metabolism. A number of companies are developing new technologies to improve transdermal absorption. A few examples of very successful transdermal systemic delivery systems include the opiate pain reliever fentanyl, contraceptive patches, and clonidine for hypertension. Examples of successful drugs used for local effects include topical steroids, antibiotics and local anesthetics.

2.9.4 Biologics Require New Delivery and Formulation Methods

The rapid increase in the number of biologics already on the market or in the pipeline has resulted in a dramatic increase in the development of new technologies to improve their delivery and efficacy/toxicity. A 2010 survey, conducted by Global Industry Analysts, forecasts that protein drug sales will be worth more than $158B by 2015 and expects therapeutic antibodies to emerge as the market leaders. Of new first-in-class agents approved between 1999 and 2008 and having novel molecular mechanisms of action, 50/75 (67%) were small molecules and 25/75 (33%) were biologics. Many, such as rituximab (Rituxan®), bevacizumab (Avastin®), epoetin alfa (Epogen®), and etanercept (Enbrel®) are multibillion dollar markets, and several are coming off patent in the next few years. This has resulted in an emerging market to devise parenteral formulations to produce so-called "bio-betters" that require less frequent administration and have an improved therapeutic index. A recent survey found that there are more than 20 independent drug delivery companies doing research on controlled release depot injection formulations, along with most of the major pharmaceutical companies that have internal programs. The formulation technologies that are being explored in these efforts to deliver biologics include microspheres, liposomes, microparticles, gels, and liquid depots (see examples listed in Box 2.30). Currently there are 13 depot products on the market, and the market size for such products is estimated to be >$2 billion dollars.

Box 2.28: What Surprised an Academician?

A formulation consultant suggested that we formulate our intracoronary drug at pH 3, as the drug was more stable in acidic conditions. Supporting his arguments, he cited a few drugs on the market. Luckily, our clinical director knew that the drugs mentioned produced phlebitis and helped me, the basic researcher, to push back on that formulation recommendation. Consultants are not always right and, if something does not seem right, we should do our own diligence. *–DM-R*

Box 2.29: The Bottom Line

There is a process of trial and error leading to the identification of optimal formulation. Understanding the clinical setting and drug dosing for the patients is critical for proper formulation development. Compromise may be required to fit the pharmacodynamics and chemical properties of the API.

Box 2.30: Suggested Resources

Reviews:

- Liechty WB, Kryscio DR, Slaughter BV and Peppas NA (2010) Polymers for Drug Delivery Systems. Annual Review of Chemical and Biomolecular Engineering. 1:149–173. (Broad and comprehensive review of this topic. Contains 149 references and other related resources)
- Wang AZ, Langer R, Farokhzad OS (2012) Nanoparticle Delivery of Cancer Drugs. Annual Review of Medicine 63: 185.
- Timko BP, Whitehead K, Gao W, Kohane DS, Farokhzad OC, Anderson D, Langer R (2011) Advances in Drug Delivery. Annual Review of Materials Research 41: 1. (This review discusses critical aspects in the area of drug delivery. Specifically, it focuses on delivery of siRNA, remote-controlled delivery, noninvasive delivery, and nanotechnology in drug delivery.)

Book:

- Rowland M, Tozer TN (2011) Clinical Pharmacokinetics and Pharmacodynamics: Concepts and Applications, 4th Edition. Wolters Kluwer/ Lippincott Williams and Wilkins, ISBN 978-0-7817-5009-7. (These authors and this book are recognized worldwide as the authorities in teaching the basic principles of pharmacokinetics and pharmacodynamics. Each chapter contains Study Problems (with answers!) and by purchasing the text can be accessed anywhere that you have an internet connection. Pharmacokinetics and pharmacodynamics simulations are also available on the Web site.)

Web sites:

- NIH Clinical Center "Principles of Clinical Pharmacology"
- http://www.cc.nih.gov/training/training/principles.html
- (This course is taught by faculty members from the National Institutes of Health (NIH) and guest faculty from the Food and Drug Administration (FDA), the pharmaceutical industry, and several academic institutions from across the USA. Course materials are available online via the above URL.)
- American College of Clinical Pharmacology, Educational Offerings
- http://www.accp1.org/videos.shtml

(continued)

Box 2.30 (continued)

- (This Web site has a free course on pharmacogenomics, covering 13 different modules, each having *overview* and *depth* sections. There is also a Web-based course on pharmacometrics.)

2.10 Preclinical Safety Studies

Michael Taylor and Kevin Grimes

"*Primum non nocere*," translates from Latin to "First, do no harm." This fundamental ethical principle in the practice of medicine is equally applicable when exposing individuals to investigational drugs. Virtually all substances can be toxic to human beings if the dose is high enough. Even drinking excessive quantities of water or breathing 100% oxygen for prolonged periods can result in severe organ damage or death. Therefore, when administering a novel compound to human subjects, we have both an ethical and legal duty to ensure that the risk has been minimized as much as possible.

Safety is difficult to prove without extensive human exposure. Lack of safety, on the other hand, can be proven. We perform preclinical safety studies to better characterize the likely effects and the risk/benefit ratio of administering a novel compound to humans. While experiments using cell lines and animal models will not mirror with certainty what will happen in human subjects, the results can be extremely helpful in predicting dose-limiting side effects and appropriate dose ranges.

The US Food and Drug Administration (FDA) and the International Committee on Harmonization (ICH) have developed guidance documents that outline a series of *in vitro* and *in vivo* experiments that should be conducted prior to each phase of clinical development for a new molecular entity (NME). These studies help predict the drug's on-target and off-target toxicities, reversibility of these toxicities, limits on the dose and duration of treatment, early predictors or signals of impending serious toxicity, and safety margin between the doses where efficacy and dose-limiting toxicity occur. Additional studies are performed to further characterize the drug's pharmacologic effects on major organ systems, pharmacokinetics, metabolism, and likely interactions with food or other drugs. Preclinical safety studies that will be submitted to regulatory agencies to support subsequent clinical testing must be performed according to Good Laboratory Practice (GLP). GLP studies require extensive documentation of each study procedure and are quite costly.

Box 2.31: Key Terms and Abbreviations

FDA: US Food and Drug Administration
ICH: International Committee on Harmonization; joint effort of European, Japanese, and US regulatory authorities and pharmaceutical industries to provide uniform standards and guidance regarding drug development
NME: New Molecular Entity; a new drug submitted to the FDA Center for Drug Evaluation and Research (CDER)
GLP: Good Laboratory Practice; extensive documentation of each procedural step to ensure high quality, reproducible studies
C_{max}: peak plasma level of a drug that is achieved after dosing
AUC: Area under the curve; plasma concentration of a drug integrated over time after dosing
Excipients: inactive materials (e.g., fillers, binders, coatings) included in the drug product formulation
API: Active Pharmaceutical Ingredient

Although there is always opportunity for discussion and negotiation, the FDA (and other regulatory agencies) typically requires a specific battery of nonclinical safety studies to be completed before advancing to phase 1 human studies. In general, the duration of drug exposure in animal studies should equal or exceed that of subsequent clinical studies. Therefore, additional general animal toxicology studies of longer durations are often performed to support increasing duration of clinical dosing prior to phase 2 and phase 3 studies. Specific studies of relatively long duration assessing reproductive toxicity and carcinogenicity are generally required before exposing large numbers of patients to study drugs in phase 3 studies.

The guidance documents include discussions of various types of studies to assess specific toxicities including safety pharmacology of the cardiovascular, pulmonary, and neurologic systems; genotoxicity; reproductive toxicity; and carcinogenicity. In addition, they outline preclinical safety requirements for specific disease indications (e.g., oncology).

In addition to identifying possible toxicities, nonclinical safety studies are also important for identifying potential biomarkers for monitoring untoward effects, establishing the first dose to be administered to humans, and establishing the upper limits of dosing (exposure) in humans. This latter purpose is particularly important when severe or non-monitorable toxicities are encountered.

Guidance regarding the development of approved drugs for new indications, by comparison, is limited. Specifically, there is a guidance that speaks to the kind of animal studies that are required for reformulated old drugs (also termed repurposing or repositioning). There is also an FDA expectation that an old drug being developed for a new indication meet current regulatory standards.

Before conducting animal studies, it is important to define how the drug will be given to patients: formulation, route of administration, and frequency of dosing. Generally speaking, animal testing should make use of the same formulation and route of dosing to be used clinically. Both the excipients (inactive ingredients of the final formulation) and active pharmaceutical ingredient (API) need to be considered and evaluated. It is important to appreciate that excipients are scrutinized during the approval process similarly to the drug under development.

When determining which excipients to include in the final formulation, the FDA inactive ingredients listing can be useful. A novel excipient or novel use, outside the limits of its current use (e.g., route, dose), will normally require additional evaluation. The use of some excipients is limited by toxicity (e.g., dimethylacetamide, cyclodextrin) and therefore it is necessary to carefully consider the excipient dose and the patient population for which the product is intended. A good strategy for excipient evaluation is to use the clinical formulation without API as the vehicle formulation (control group) in animal studies. It is also advisable to include an additional negative control group, to confirm lack of effects by the excipient.

The selection of the API lot for animal testing is also important. The tested material should be representative of the material intended for clinical use, such that the impurity profile should be both qualitatively and quantitatively similar to the clinical material. There are several guidances that discuss the acceptable limits of API impurities and the necessary steps for impurity qualification when such limits are surpassed. A good practice, particularly for the IND-enabling studies, is to use the same lot of API for nonclinical safety studies that is to be used in the clinic.

Box 2.32: What Surprised an Academician?

The drug tested in GLP toxicity studies should not be too pure. If the clinical lot has higher levels of impurities than the toxicology lot, which can occur from manufacture scale up, further GLP toxicology studies will be required to characterize the potential toxic effects of the new or increased impurities. This can significantly impact development timelines and budgets. So it took me some time to understand, when told by the VP of Drug Development, that my pride in purifying our non-GLP material to 99.5% purity before using it in pig efficacy studies was misguided and potentially a very costly mistake. *–DM-R*

Appropriate dose selection is important to the conduct of useful and therefore successful animal studies. In part, success should be considered based on efficient use of animals. Although the use of two species of animal models is central to drug development and evaluation, there is an ever-increasing awareness and responsibility to follow humane practices and to thoroughly justify the need for animal use and numbers.

The fundamental premise of dose selection for animal studies is that the animal doses and exposures (C_{max}, AUC) should exceed those proposed for humans.

Ideally, the high dose for animal studies is best selected by clear evidence of toxicity, such as decreased body weight gain, changes in clinical condition, or abnormalities in clinical pathology parameters. The low dose should be a small multiple (2–3×) of the projected clinical dose (exposure) and the mid dose should be set between the high and low doses. It is important to separate doses such that the exposures between groups do not overlap. For many orally delivered small molecules or parenterally delivered macromolecules, doses can be adequately spread using half log or log intervals. Since there is less pharmacokinetic variability for intravenous administration, the dose intervals can be smaller.

Because both dose and time influence toxicity, it is difficult to predict doses that will be tolerated for chronic administration. Therefore, it is best to plan studies of increasing duration sequentially. Selection of doses for the first studies can be challenging and one should draw on all available information. Whereas rodents are usually the species chosen for the early efficacy studies, there is typically no information available for dosing in the non-rodent model. If no or limited data are available, short duration non-GLP pilot studies (1–3 days) with minimal numbers of animals should be performed to assist in selecting the appropriate dose range. For compounds with limited evidence of toxicity, the high dose can be set based upon consideration of the animal exposure relative to humans and practical limits such as dose volume or API solubility.

This discussion provides an introduction to the types and extent of preclinical safety studies required to support drug development. Please also consult the previous sections on formulation and drug metabolism, as these are also important considerations for successful safety evaluation.

Box 2.33: The Bottom Line

When administering a novel compound to human subjects, we have both an ethical and legal duty to ensure that the risk has been minimized as much as possible. Preclinical safety studies help to minimize risk to human subjects by identifying potential toxicities, appropriate dosing ranges, and early signals of toxicity.

Box 2.34: Resources

Specific FDA guidance on Nonclinical Safety Studies:
http://www.fda.gov/downloads/Drugs/GuidanceComplianceRegulatoryInformation/Guidances/UCM073246.pdf

References

1. Begley CG, Ellis LM (2012) Raising standards for preclinical cancer research. Nature 483:531–533
2. Prinz F, Schlange T, Asadullah K (2011) Believe it or not: how much can we rely on published data on potential drug target? Nat Rev Drug Discov 10:328–329
3. King C, Sarvetnick N (2011) The incidence of type-1 diabetes in NOD mice is modulated by restricted flora not germ-free conditions. PLoS ONE 6:e17049
4. Begley CG (2013) Six red flags for suspect work. Nature 497:433–434
5. Peers IS, Ceuppens PR, Harborn C (2012) In search of preclinical robustness. Nat Rev Drug Discov 11:733–734
6. Kneller R (2010) The importance of new companies for drug discovery: origins of a decade of new drugs. Nat Rev Drug Discov 9:867–882
7. Code of federal regulations, title 21 food and drugs, subchapter D drugs for human use, part 312, subpart B investigational new drug application, 312.2
8. Huang R, Southall N, Wang Y et al (2011) The NCGC pharmaceutical collection: a comprehensive resource of clinically approved drugs enabling repurposing and chemical genomics. Sci Transl Med 3:80ps16
9. Collins FS (2011) Reengineering translational science: the time is right. Sci Transl Med 3:90cm17
10. Zhang JH, Chung TDY, Oldenburg KR (1999) A simple statistical parameter for use in evaluation and validation of high throughput screening assays. J Biomol Screen 4:67–73
11. Copeland RA (2003) Mechanistic considerations in high-throughput screening. Anal Biochem 320:1–12
12. Wu G, Yuan Y, Hodge CN (2003) Determining appropriate substrate conversion for enzymatic assays in high-throughput screening. J Biomol Screen 8(6):694–700
13. Lipinski CA, Lombardo F, Dominy BW, Feeney PJ (1997) Experimental and computational approaches to estimate solubility and permeability in drug discovery and development settings. Adv Drug Delivery Rev 23:3–25
14. Rydzewski RM (2008) Real world drug discovery: a chemist's guide to biotech and pharmaceutical research. Elsevier Science, Oxford, Chapter 9
15. Ekroos M, Sjogren T (2006) Structural basis for ligand promiscuity in cytochrome P450 3A4. PNAS 103:13682–13687

Chapter 3
Preparing for the Clinic

Daria Mochly-Rosen and Kevin Grimes

Transitioning from preclinical to clinical development can be both an exhilarating and a sobering experience. Presumably, our drug has passed through a rigorous battery of preclinical testing and appears to have the desired safety profile and pharmacologic characteristics for advancement to human study. But embarking upon human experimentation is a serious undertaking. We must ensure that our clinical trial is designed and conducted in as safe a manner as possible. We have an ethical responsibility to ensure that our clinical trial has been designed to optimize the probability of obtaining meaningful results since we are exposing human subjects to a potentially toxic new molecular entity. Furthermore, the drug must be manufactured and quality-tested using exacting standards, typically by a reputable contract manufacturing organization (CMO). Both the Food and Drug Administration (FDA) and Institutional Review Boards (or Ethics Committees outside of the USA) seek to ensure that patients are protected and that the risk-to-benefit ratio is acceptable for any clinical study. Early in the planning process, the development team should engage experts in drug manufacturing and quality control, clinical trial design, and regulatory science. Before the clinical trial can commence, the sponsor (company or physician) must file an Investigational New Drug application (IND) with the FDA. The IND provides detailed information on the nonclinical pharmacology and safety studies, the drug manufacturing and quality assurance (QA) process, and the clinical trial protocol. This chapter provides an overview of clinical trial design, acquisition of clinical grade drug product, and regulatory considerations during the transition into the clinic. Because clinical trials are so

D. Mochly-Rosen (✉)
Chemical and Systems Biology, Stanford University School of Medicine, 269 Campus Drive, Center for Clinical Science Research Rm 3145a, Stanford, CA 94305-5174, USA
e-mail: sparkmed@stanford.edu

K. Grimes
Chemical and Systems Biology, Stanford University School of Medicine, 269 Campus Drive, Center for Clinical Science Research Rm 3145c, Stanford, CA 94305-5174, USA
e-mail: kgrimes@stanford.edu

D. Mochly-Rosen and K. Grimes (eds.), *A Practical Guide to Drug Development in Academia*, SpringerBriefs in Pharmaceutical Science & Drug Development,
DOI 10.1007/978-3-319-02201-7_3,

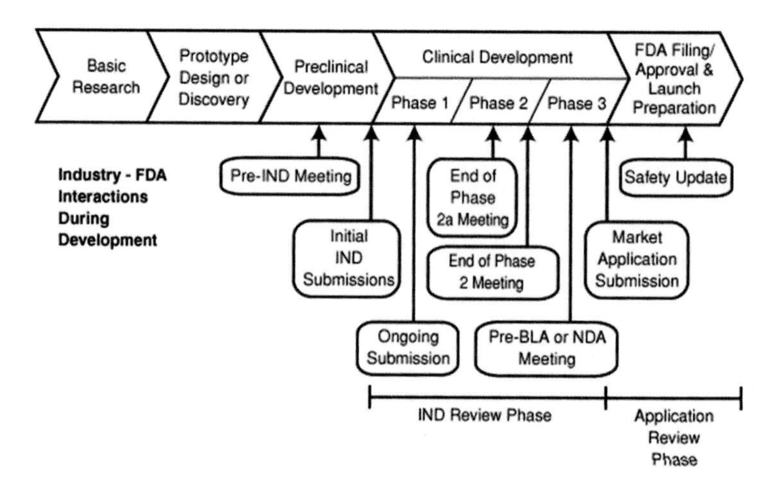

Fig. 3.1 Drug development pipeline and FDA regulatory steps. Source: FDA

expensive, failure to appropriately design the clinical trial can obscure efficacy and force a program to close. Even seasoned clinicians would be wise to talk with other experts before embarking on a clinical trial.

3.1 Regulatory Considerations in Product Development

Carol Karp

When determining the regulatory pathway for the development of a new therapeutic, it is essential to consider the overall risk-to-benefit profile, target disease, patient population, and claims for the product. As a general rule, the broader the target population or product claims, the greater the burden of evidence that will be required. The optimal regulatory approach for a specific product should be adapted based upon these key considerations (Fig. 3.1).

The Prescription Drug User Fee Act (PDUFA) was originally enacted in 1992, enabling the FDA to collect fees from companies submitting applications for the marketing of human drug and biological products. At a stakeholder meeting in March 2011 on PDUFA V for reauthorization of the Act, the FDA cited the average total time from discovery to product approval as 12 years, with an average total cost of $1 billion. The 2013 fee for submission of a New Drug Application (NDA) or Biologic License Application (BLA) to the FDA under PDUFA V is $1,958,800.

Box 3.1: Key Terms and Abbreviations

PDUFA: Prescription Drug User Fee Act; US legislation that changed how the FDA collected fees
FDA: Food and Drug Administration; the Federal Health and Human Services agency responsible for protecting the public health
CDER: FDA Center for Drug Evaluation and Research; responsible for promoting the safe and effective use of drugs
CBER: FDA Center for Biologics Evaluation and Research; responsible for the regulation of biological and related products such as vaccines, blood, cellular and gene therapy
CDRH: FDA Center for Devices and Radiological Health; responsible for ensuring the safety and effectiveness of medical devices and limiting unnecessary radiological exposure
IND: Investigational New Drug application; document filed with the FDA prior to initiating research on human subjects using any drug that has not been previously approved for the proposed clinical indication, dosing regimen, or patient population
NDA: New Drug Application; FDA paperwork to obtain approval for the sales and marketing of a new drug in the USA
BLA: Biologics License Application; FDA paperwork to obtain approval for the sales and marketing of a new biologic in the USA
Therapeutic BLA: BLA application for a product such as a monoclonal antibody or growth factor, submitted to CDER
CTD: Common Technical Document; standardized five-module format for regulatory applications in the USA, EU, and Japan
Sponsor or Applicant: The individual or entity that submits an IND or NDA

3.1.1 Investigational New Drug (IND) Application

The first step for initiation of clinical studies for a new product is the submission of an IND to the FDA. Key components of an IND consist of the following: (1) Nonclinical pharmacology and toxicology summaries and study reports to demonstrate that the investigational drug is reasonably safe for initial testing in human subjects. When repurposing a previously approved product, this may entail support for testing of a new dose level, route of administration, patient population or target disease; (2) Quality information, referred to as Chemistry, Manufacturing and Controls (CMC), to demonstrate that the clinical trial material can be adequately produced and supplied. This includes descriptions of the composition, source, manufacture, testing, specifications and stability of the drug substance, or Active Pharmaceutical Ingredient (API), and the finished Drug Product (DP);

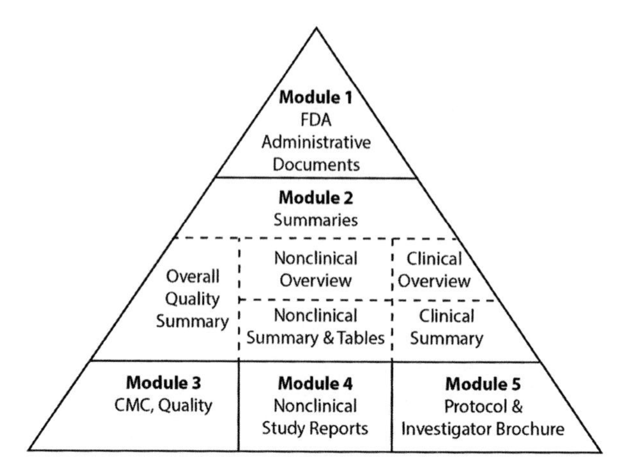

Fig. 3.2 IND organization (CTD format)

(3) Clinical information, including the proposed clinical study protocol, and identification of the clinical investigator, to assure that subjects will not be exposed to unnecessary risks and to confirm the qualifications and commitment of the investigator(s); (4) the general investigational plan for clinical studies over the next year; and (5) the Investigator's Brochure, which provides investigators with a compilation of preclinical, clinical and CMC data, and guidance on the study rationale, dosing regimen and clinical management, including safety monitoring.

An IND is submitted to the FDA as a CTD, or Common Technical Document, the accepted electronic or paper format for both INDs and NDAs, and for equivalent submissions in the EU and Japan (Fig. 3.2).

The CTD format allows the IND to begin forming the building blocks for what may eventually become an NDA to obtain FDA approval for marketing of the product upon successful completion of a clinical program. The initial IND review is a 30-day process that encompasses assessments by FDA medical, chemistry, and pharmacology/toxicology reviewers to determine if the initial clinical study can be safely conducted.

Typically, a sponsoring pharmaceutical or biotech company submits an IND. Alternatively, in an academic setting, a physician may submit an investigator-initiated IND. In this case, the sponsoring physician both initiates and conducts the clinical investigation. The investigational drug must be administered or dispensed under the immediate direction of the sponsoring physician.

3.1.2 IND Special Cases

Exemptions from the requirement for an IND may apply to clinical studies of approved drug products that do not involve new routes of administration, dosing levels, patient populations, or other factors that might significantly increase the risks associated with the approved marketed use of the product.

In addition, a number of expedited approaches for the development and review of new drug products have been made available by the FDA. An exploratory IND can allow for the screening of multiple closely related active moieties to identify the preferred compound or formulation to be taken forward for development under a formal IND. This approach is intended to provide greater flexibility for early phase 1 screening or microdose studies for the assessment of attributes such as mechanism of action or pharmacokinetics. Given the limited human exposure, such studies can be initiated with a less extensive preclinical program than that required for a traditional IND.

Fast track is an FDA program spanning both the IND and NDA development stages for products with the potential to address (1) a serious or life-threatening condition and (2) an unmet medical need. Fast track designation may be requested at initial IND submission or at any point prior to NDA (or BLA) marketing approval. Fast track is an overarching regulatory approach that can include the following: (1) close ongoing communication with the FDA from pre-IND through pre-NDA meetings, (2) rolling review of sections of an application by the FDA in advance of the complete NDA submission, (3) priority review, providing for a shorter FDA review period of an NDA, and (4) accelerated approval, which enables the FDA approval based upon a surrogate endpoint that is reasonably likely to predict clinical benefit. In 2012, the FDA established a new Breakthrough Therapy program for a drug intended to treat a serious or life-threatening disease and with preliminary clinical evidence suggesting that a substantial improvement in one or more relevant clinical endpoints over current treatment options may be provided. Breakthrough therapy designation provides all of the benefits of fast track status, in addition to intensive FDA guidance, involving senior managers and experienced reviewers, to support the conduct of efficient clinical trials and to expedite the overall development program.

3.1.3 Meeting with the FDA

Meetings between the FDA and a sponsor or applicant of an IND or NDA are not required but are often encouraged to obtain FDA guidance at critical points during the drug development process. A pre-IND meeting provides an opportunity for the development team to familiarize themselves with the approach to these meetings and can be held either as a teleconference or face-to-face.

The pre-IND meeting request, about a 3 page document, includes the product name, chemical structure, proposed indication, objectives of the meeting, proposed agenda, list of specific questions, list of participants for the sponsor and requested FDA participants. A background package of about 50–100 pages is submitted in advance of the meeting and includes (1) an introduction of the product concept, (2) the proposed indication, (3) an overview of the development plans, (4) a summary of the pharmacology and toxicology studies that have been conducted, (5) initial plans for additional nonclinical studies, (6) a summary of information available on the drug substance and drug product, (7) initial clinical development plans, (8) a synopsis of the initial clinical study protocol, and (9) specific questions or issues.

Box 3.2: Pre-IND Meeting Target Time Frames

Day 0: Submit meeting request
Day 14: FDA response to request
Day 30: Submit Background Package
Day 60: Pre-IND meeting

Pre-IND, end-of-phase 2, pre-phase 3, and pre-NDA meetings are classified as Type B meetings. Type A meetings are generally reserved for situations such as a clinical hold, when FDA has determined that a clinical study cannot be initiated or continued. Type C meetings are those not covered by Type A or Type B.

Box 3.3: Target Time Frame from FDA Receipt of Written Request to Meeting

Type A: 30 Days
Type B: 60 Days
Type C: 75 Days

3.1.4 New Drug Application (NDA)

NDAs, the applications to obtain FDA approval to market drug products in the USA, are based upon the nonclinical, clinical, and CMC data generated during the IND development stage. An NDA enables the FDA to determine whether: (1) the drug is safe and effective for its proposed use and the benefits outweigh the risks, (2) the proposed product labeling is appropriate and adequate, and (3) the manufacturing methods and controls to maintain product quality are adequate.

For a drug product intended for chronic treatment of a non-life-threatening condition, the extent of population exposure to support approval is approximately 1,500 patients, with 100 patients treated for $\geq$12 months and 300–600 patients treated for $\geq$6 months. For each new product, the regulatory pathway and overall burden of evidence should be considered in the context of the target disease, patient population, product claims and overall benefit/risk profile.

Box 3.4: The Bottom Line

The FDA performs a critical role in ensuring that new drugs are both safe and effective. A collegial working relationship with the agency and familiarity with applicable regulations and guidelines can facilitate the transition from lab bench to clinic and increase the probability of success for a development program.

Box 3.5: Resources

1. FDA Regulations: IND Content and Format http://www.accessdata.fda.gov/scripts/cdrh/cfdocs/cfcfr/CFRSearch.cfm?fr=312.23
2. FDA Guidance for Industry: Organization of the CTD http://www.fda.gov/downloads/Drugs/GuidanceComplianceRegulatoryInformation/Guidances/UCM073257.pdf
3. FDA Guidance for Industry: INDs: Determining whether Human Research Studies can be conducted without an IND http://www.fda.gov/downloads/Drugs/GuidanceComplianceRegulatoryInformation/Guidances/UCM229175.pdf
4. FDA Guidance for Industry, Investigators and Reviewers: Exploratory IND Studies http://www.fda.gov/downloads/Drugs/GuidanceComplianceRegulatoryInformation/Guidances/UCM078933.pdf
5. FDA Guidance for Industry: Fast Track Drug Development Programs http://www.fda.gov/downloads/Drugs/GuidanceComplianceRegulatoryInformation/Guidances/UCM079736.pdf
6. FDA Draft Guidance for Industry: Expedited Programs for Serious Conditions—Drugs and Biologics http://www.fda.gov/downloads/Drugs/GuidanceComplianceRegulatoryInformation/Guidances/UCM358301.pdf
7. FDA Guidance for Industry: Formal Meetings between the FDA and Sponsors or Applicants http://www.fda.gov/downloads/Drugs/GuidanceComplianceRegulatoryInformation/Guidances/UCM153222.pdf
8. ICH Guideline for Industry: Extent of Exposure to Assess Clinical Safety http://www.fda.gov/downloads/Drugs/GuidanceComplianceRegulatoryInformation/Guidances/UCM073083.pdf

3.2 Manufacturing and Quality Control

Susan Wade

3.2.1 Regulatory Considerations

The manufacturing of drugs is regulated by the FDA in the USA, by the European Medicines Agency (EMA) in the European Union, by the Pharmaceuticals and Medical Devices Agency (PMDA) in Japan, and by various other regulatory agencies throughout the world. The International Conference on Harmonisation of Technical Requirements for Registration of Pharmaceuticals for Human Use

(ICH) represents an ongoing effort by the regulatory authorities and pharmaceutical trade organizations of the USA, Europe, and Japan to harmonize drug regulatory requirements.

Nonetheless, the regulatory requirements for clinical drug supplies can and do vary by geographic region. When planning clinical studies, the drug supply must meet the regulatory requirements for each country in which the study will be conducted. While the national regulatory agencies and ICH have published guidance documents, discussions with the individual regulatory agencies can also be helpful during the planning process.

If studies are planned in the USA only, the products will need to be approved and released by a QA group that is independent of the manufacturing function. If studies are planned in the European Union, the products will need to be released by a licensed "Qualified Person" (QP). These quality groups must certify that the products meet predetermined specifications and were manufactured according to the applicable "Good Manufacturing Practice" (GMP).

Box 3.6: Key Terms and Abbreviations

IND: Investigational New Drug application; document filed with the FDA prior to initiating research on human subjects using any drug that has not been previously approved for the proposed clinical indication, dosing regimen, or patient population
EMA: European Medicines Agency
QA: Quality Assurance
QC: Quality Control
QP: Qualified Person
GMP: Good Manufacturing Practice; exacting procedures and documentation of quality assurance carried out at a certified facility (sometimes referred to as "cGMP" for "current" practice)
QSR: Quality System Regulations
NIST: National Institute of Standards and Technology
Master Batch Record: Written performance of all manufacturing and testing methods that have been approved by QA
CAPA: Corrective and Preventive Actions
Validation (or qualification of) assays: a formal process, demonstrating that an assay is specific, reproducible and precise.
Stability indicating assay: Often done at a higher temperature than the recommended storage temperature, where stability is determined over time.
ICH: International Conference on Harmonisation; organization that provides international guidelines for drug testing
CMO: Contract Manufacturing Organization
API: Active Pharmaceutical Ingredient

(continued)

Box 3.6 (continued)

Drug Product: API and inactive components such as binders, capsule, etc. that compose the final drug formulation
RFP: Request for Proposal
CMC: Chemistry, Manufacturing and Controls
Master File: FDA file certifying a manufacturing company based on prior IND submissions establishing GMP requirements

3.2.2 Manufacturing Requirements

Facilities that manufacture drugs for clinical trials must operate in compliance with applicable GMP. The US drug GMP regulations are published in the Code of Federal Regulations under 21 CFR 210 and 211 "Good Manufacturing Practice." These regulations require documentation of all aspects of the manufacturing process.

Key points in the GMP requirements include the following:

- There must be an independent QA function.
- All materials used in manufacturing must be traceable to the original manufacturer and lot number.
- Inventories must be maintained, documenting use of all raw materials and components.
- There must be documented evidence that operators are educated and trained in all functions needed to perform their duties.
- All equipment used must be calibrated using National Institute of Standards and Technology (NIST) traceable standards.
- Performance of each manufacturing step must be documented and critical steps must also be witnessed, as evidenced by dated signature.
- The manufacturing and testing methods must be written and approved by management and the QA officer prior to performing the manufacturing. This is typically called a Master Batch Record.
- Any deviations to the written methods must be documented and approved by the QA officer.
- The product specifications must be written and approved prior to testing of the product.
- The product must meet the predetermined specifications.
- Quality systems including internal audits, Corrective and Preventive Actions (CAPA), scheduled management reviews, and a quality manual must be in place.

In addition to these basic requirements, there are many additional regulations specific to biologics, sterile products, devices, botanicals, extended release formulations, etc. It is very important to have someone familiar with the type of product and the applicable regulations assist in identification of an appropriate manufacturer.

Box 3.7: What Surprised an Academician?

Early in our phase 2a clinical trial with the first compound, our VP of Drug Development decided to manufacture a new batch of GMP material in spite of the fact that we had plenty made for the trial size. This was a huge expense and I pushed back on it, thinking it was wasteful. When our first batch failed specifications with unacceptable levels of degradation due to the slow enrollment of our trial, it took KAI two days to retrieve the old drug from the sites and switch to the new batch. Planning for failure and building contingencies were critical for the success of the trial. *–DM-R*

3.2.3 Testing Requirements

Drugs used in clinical studies must be tested to assure they meet pre-approved specifications. This testing typically includes some measure of potency, assays for manufacturing contaminants, and assays for degradation products. If the API has chiral centers, testing for enantiomer purity may be warranted. In addition, depending on the dosage form, safety tests for sterility, bioburden, endotoxin, and heavy metals may also be required.

Assays used to test commercial products must be "validated"; validation is a formal process of demonstrating that the assay performs as intended and is specific, reproducible and precise. Assays used for testing products intended for use in clinical trials must be documented to be scientifically sound - this is often referred to as "qualified." The use of these terms varies significantly from company to company; so make sure to ask exactly what is meant.

3.2.4 Stability Testing

There must be data available to assure that products used in clinical testing are stable throughout the duration of the trial. If this is an existing product for a new use, such data may already exist. However, stability testing must be conducted for a new product. Typically, a stability-indicating assay is developed and qualified to be able to detect degradation products. Forced degradation studies attempt to accelerate product degradation by exposure to stressful storage conditions, usually excess heat or moisture. In many cases, a high-performance liquid chromatography (HPLC) assay is included to detect degradation products.

It is usually acceptable to submit 3 months of stability testing on the lot of GMP product that is going to be used in the clinic under an Investigational New Drug (IND). "Supportive" stability studies that were performed on research grade product prior to manufacture of the GMP clinical supplies can also be included. Stability testing of the GMP clinical product must continue during the clinical trial period.

Typically, stability testing is performed at 3, 6, 9, 12, 18, 24, and 36 months, as described in the ICH Stability Guidelines. Quality control must monitor the results of the stability testing in real time and remove any product that does not continue to meet specifications from clinical use.

Box 3.8: What Surprised an Academician?

I was surprised one afternoon to find hundreds of drug vials on the precious lab space that I secured for our new hire at KAI. When told that they were running a stability study, I was further irritated; I had already performed an HPLC run of a compound that we saved in the fridge for a few months in my lab at Stanford University. Why repeat it and why in my precious lab space?! The reason is that the experimental rigor and degree of documentation for this study far exceeded what I had thought was necessary. *–DM-R*

3.2.5 Selecting a Contract Manufacturing Organization

There are two very important considerations when selecting a CMO:

1. Do they have quality systems and GMP manufacturing processes in place for preparation of clinical supplies?
2. Do they have experience developing and manufacturing the dosage form you need?

You absolutely do not want the group learning these basics on your project. You are paying for both technical expertise and regulatory compliance.

Ideally, you will be able to find an expert advisor that is familiar with this type of manufacturing to help identify an appropriate CMO. If not, search Google® using key words such as GMP, clinical supplies, and dosage form (sterile, parenteral, oral, cream, etc.) Try various combinations until you find the appropriate companies. Prepare a "Request for Proposal (RFP)" that you can send to the companies, indicating what services you need such as manufacturing, QC testing, stability testing, and/or packaging. Be sure to include specifics about your desired product. For example, specify whether you are asking for pure API or finished Drug Product. Provide details including availability of starting materials such as API, quantity of product you need delivered (after sampling and testing), and time frame for the project. Request a detailed quote with the pricing broken down for each activity. Once the company has carefully read your RFP, a teleconference can be a helpful next step. After you have compared quotes, you will typically need to go back to the companies for clarifications. It is advisable to visit the CMO site in person with your expert advisor.

3.2.6 CMC Section of the IND

The Chemistry, Manufacturing, and Controls (CMC) section of the IND must include a detailed description of the manufacturing and testing of the product. This section of the filing will also include product specifications, a Certificate of Analysis for each product lot to be used in the clinic and a stability protocol. A list of all facilities involved in the manufacturing, testing, holding, and distribution of the product is also required. Occasionally, you may be performing clinical testing using product that is manufactured by a company that holds a "Master File" with the FDA from previous filings. Under such circumstances, the CMC section can be replaced by a reference to the "Master File."

Box 3.9: The Bottom Line

Although the regulatory requirements for manufacturing and quality assurance seem rather elaborate, they exist to protect both patients and drug manufacturers. Consistency of drug product is essential for reproducible clinical studies that demonstrate both safety and efficacy. These standards underscore a critically important issue: aggressive quality control is not only good science, but helps ensure the safety of the experimental subjects (the patients).

3.3 Technical Development and Manufacturing of Biological Products

Mark Backer

The development of biological products, or "large molecules," has important differences from drugs created by synthetic chemistry. The preparations for supporting a proposed clinical testing plan must address the same categories as small molecules, as outlined in IND guidance documents, but the nature of these activities can be substantially different based on the production methods and product characteristics that are associated with biologicals. An overview of early stage biological product development is provided here, with a focus on manufacturing, testing and regulatory expectations.

The technical and regulatory foundation for modern biological products was established by the development of life-saving vaccines and protein replacement therapies such as bovine insulin. These products were derived from animals, and regulators quickly learned that the benefits of these products were balanced by some new complexities and risks because of the potential for variability or unwanted contaminants derived from the biological source. With the advent of eggs and then aseptic cell culture for vaccine production, followed by recombinant DNA (rDNA) technology in the late 1970s and monoclonal antibody technology in the 1980s, it became possible to produce a much wider variety of biological products with improved control over product consistency and safety. Still, the biological origin and the natural heterogeneity of these products require a different development approach compared to small molecules.

In the early days of biological products, a guiding philosophy was "the process is the product"; in other words, process changes were discouraged because the product could not be characterized well. Potential effects on product quality and safety could not be easily assessed without repeating clinical trials. Now, a framework is in place to support process evolution and even biosimilar products, but this depends on thorough comparability analysis of drug characteristics.

Biological products include a wide variety of product types; at one extreme some small peptides and nucleic acid products can in fact be manufactured by nonbiological synthesis. At the other extreme, live viruses and even whole cells have been developed as commercial products. The development approach needs to be adapted for each type of product. As an introduction, this discussion will focus on recombinant protein products and monoclonal antibodies, which are the most common.

Box 3.10: Key Terms and Abbreviations

rDNA: Recombinant DNA; DNA constructs that have been artificially manipulated and do not naturally occur in organisms
Biosimilar: generic version of a previously approved biologic therapeutic
GMP: Good Manufacturing Practice; exacting procedures and documentation of quality assurance carried out at a certified facility (sometimes referred to as "cGMP" for "current" practice)
MCB: Master Cell Bank; repository of frozen cell aliquots for the clonal hybridoma line selected for biological product manufacture
WCB: Working Cell Bank; frozen aliquots of cells for active use in manufacture and testing
Drug Substance: the pharmacologically active biological material
API: Active pharmaceutical ingredient; the pharmacologically active small molecule
Drug Product: the final formulation of pharmacologically active molecule plus any inactive binders and excipients
Media fill: manufacturing run using media performed to demonstrate sterile operations
CMC: Chemistry, Manufacturing and Controls
TSE: Transmissible spongiform encephalopathy
CMO: Contract manufacturing organization
BLA: Biologics License Application filed with the FDA; the biologic product equivalent to a New Drug Application
HC: Heavy chain of antibody
LC: Light chain of antibody

3.3.1 Expression Systems

The first biological products that used rDNA technology were produced in *E. coli* bacteria, for example human insulin and growth hormone. These products established the approach for diverting the *E. coli* biological machinery to manufacture the protein of interest using a plasmid that includes a promoter driving expression of a DNA transgene encoding the target protein. Microbial expression systems are popular because they can generate large amounts of recombinant protein thanks to strong translation machinery and dense culture conditions. There are some limitations though. Large mammalian proteins that feature numerous disulfide cross-links, glycosylation, or posttranslational modifications generally cannot be manufactured in *E. coli* or yeast. In addition, proper protein folding in microbial systems can be a problem, and the target protein must often be refolded after recovery from misfolded, aggregated material called inclusion bodies.

For more complex proteins and antibodies, mammalian cell culture is used for manufacturing. The first antibody products were produced by culturing hybridoma cell lines, which are created by fusing a continuous B-cell line (myeloma) with another B-cell that produces the antibody of interest. Today, the generation of a hybridoma is generally followed by transferring the antibody heavy and light chain genes to a different cell line with promoters optimized for manufacturing: murine myeloma or more typically CHO (Chinese hamster ovary) cells. The HEK293 (human embryonic kidney) cell line is also used in manufacturing recombinant proteins, and other human and animal cell lines are used to produce viral-based vaccines. A panel of candidate recombinant clones (each clone grown from a single cell) is tested for productivity and quality, and the chosen clone is expanded to create a research cell bank that serves as the basis for further testing and eventually manufacturing.

3.3.2 Preparing for Clinical Testing

Once an antibody or protein product has been tested in animal models and there is a rationale for further development, preparations for clinical testing begin. The FDA has provided guidance that outlines the expectations for sponsors' documentation and testing when using antibodies, and it is prudent to review this before making the hybridoma cell line. As an early step, the research bank is used to create a Master Cell Bank (MCB) that establishes the foundation for consistent production under GMP conditions. For pivotal trials and commercial manufacturing, a two-tiered bank system is required and a Working Cell Bank (WCB) is also produced and tested. Some sponsors produce both the MCB and WCB prior to phase 1 testing to eliminate any subsequent product comparability issues, but WCB production is often deferred to save time and money for first-in-human trials. If the manufacturing process features a virus for production of vaccine antigen or use as a genetic vector, a similar approach to banking is used (preparation of a Master Virus Seed and Working Virus Seed in addition to the MCB and WCB for the cell substrate).

3.3.3 Upstream and Downstream

Manufacturing proceeds by expanding the MCB clone from the seed stock in a series of increasingly larger vessels through the production bioreactor scale using customized growth media, in axenic culture (sterile except for the production cell line itself). Bioreactors provide tight control over oxygen levels, pH and agitation of the culture; and concentrated nutrients are added to increase cell density. Mammalian cell culture is practiced in industry at a scale up to 20,000 L of bioreactor volume, but production for phase 1 testing is conducted at a smaller scale—typically 100–1,000 L depending on the trial design and dosage. In general, fed-batch cell culture densities are in the range of 5–10 $\times$ 10^6 cells/mL and antibody titers are in the range of 1–2 g/L of bioreactor volume. For products with anticipated large demand, further optimization is usually performed prior to pivotal trials to reach titers above 4 g/L. Antibodies and recombinant proteins are excreted from the producing cells, so the product is harvested by removing the cells using a centrifuge or filter. The process steps through this stage are called the *upstream process*.

The cell-free harvest must be purified and concentrated in order to produce a composition suitable for use in humans. These *downstream process* steps generally include an affinity purification step for antibodies (using a Protein A resin for capture) and at least two column chromatography steps to separate the target protein from impurities and unwanted variants (such as aggregates, clipped proteins, and dimers). Polymer membranes that are permeable only to water and small molecular weight molecules are used for concentration and buffer exchange; these steps are called UF/DF (ultrafiltration and diafiltration). The resulting material, which should be very close to the intended clinical formulation, is called Drug Substance, similar to API, a term generally used for small molecules.

Because of the chance that a virus could be present in the producing cell line or introduced in the upstream process, extra downstream steps are performed to reduce this risk (e.g., a low pH step and nanofiltration using a filter that would remove virus). Specific viral clearance studies are performed to demonstrate that the steps effectively remove a panel of representative virus types. These studies, like testing for adventitious agents, are generally contracted out to one of a small number of industry vendors with the required capabilities and experience.

3.3.4 Drug Product

Most biological products are sterile and are administered by a parenteral route (intravenous or injection), because proteins generally do not survive to reach their

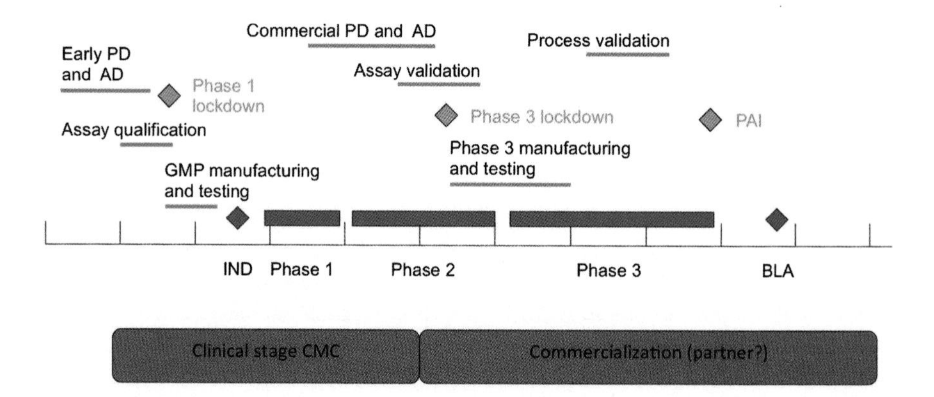

Fig. 3.3 CMC view of the path to licensure for a biological product. A typical project may take around 9 years from initiating development of a candidate to BLA filing; this Gantt chart outlines important development steps. *AD* assay development, *PD* process development, *IND* Investigational New Drug application, *GMP* Good Manufacturing Practice, *BLA* Biologics License Application, *PAI* pre-approval inspection

targets after oral administration. The drug substance is diluted or reformulated as needed, passed through a sterilizing filter, and then filled into vials or prefilled syringes in special clean rooms to maintain sterility. They are then labeled and packaged into the format needed for clinical testing. Unlike some small molecule drugs, proteins cannot be sterilized by heat or radiation, so maintaining sterility through the filling process is critical for patient safety. If the filling vendor has not recently used the same components (vials and stoppers) at a similar scale for GMP manufacturing, filling sterility must be assured in advance by performing a media fill (a dummy run using sterile media); this time and expense needs to be considered in the project plan. Biologicals may be lyophilized and reconstituted for administration (potentially a challenging development activity), but most are stored as refrigerated or frozen liquids—particularly in early development (Fig. 3.3).

3.3.5 Testing and Compliance

A successful IND requires that extensive safety testing and characterization be performed and GMP regulations followed. The term "CMC" has become an umbrella term that refers to the process development and analytical development work supporting product development, together with Manufacturing and Quality activities- rather than simply the Chemistry, Manufacturing and Controls section of the IND itself (Tables 3.1 and 3.2). There are some key considerations for biological material CMC:

- Documentation is critical. Even the construction of the Research Cell Bank should be thoroughly documented, such as the origin, lot numbers and qualification (if any) of materials that are used (gene sources or synthesis, creation of the expression construct itself, cell lines, serum, and any material of animal origin). If serum must be used at any point in development, it should be obtained from a TSE-free (transmissible spongiform encephalopathy) country such as New Zealand, and purchasing records and lot numbers retained.
- Cell lines used in the biologic construction or manufacturing should have documented origin and freedom to operate (e.g., a research license from ATCC). Clinical use of particular promoters, genetic elements or humanization methods may also trigger licensing fees or unwanted royalty obligations attached to the product—although sometimes these charges are an acceptable burden in return for enabling the best technical approach.
- Cell banks and drug substance batches need to be thoroughly tested for adventitious agents (such as unwanted viruses or bacteria) and the recombinant construct should be sequenced to assure that the correct protein sequence is produced and no extraneous sequences are present.
- The drug product used for key preclinical testing, in particular IND-enabling toxicology testing, should ideally have the same formulation, administration route and be from the same batch as that intended for clinical use. If a different batch is used, the sponsor will need to establish that the preclinical and clinical products are comparable with bridging studies.
- Reference standards should be established to support testing, and specifications established to make sure that the drug product meets regulatory expectations for identity, purity, potency and strength (strength refers to the amount of the active ingredient).
- Additional characterization may be performed that is not required as a specification; for example, analysis of carbohydrates or protein sequencing of a drug product lot.
- Formal stability testing is needed to establish that the drug product characteristics do not change before administration (see regulatory guidelines listed in Box 3.12 “Resources”).
- Tests to measure host cell protein and DNA impurities are needed. These tests are commercially available for common host cell lines, but can be complex and expensive to develop for novel culture systems.
- Most assays do not need to be validated for phase 1 studies, but key assays should be qualified and demonstrated to be scientifically sound. Assays related to safety will receive greater scrutiny.
- After manufacturing, the QA unit reviews the manufacturing batch records and test results to assure that the drug substance and drug product are within specification, and investigates any discrepancies in results or in GMP compliance. Adventitious agent testing for a biological product takes about 2 months, and it is typical for full batch release to take 3–4 months after the drug substance is produced before the product is released for clinical use.

Box 3.11: What Surprised an Academician?

In the spirit of "No task is too small" and "All employees are equal" in the early days of KAI, I unboxed a shipment of thermometers and threw away the shipment materials and other, what I considered trivial, info about the thermometers. You could later find me with the VP of Drug Development digging through the company's trash for the certificate documents that were essential to keep, as these thermometers were to be shipped to the clinical sites to ensure that the trial drug was stored at the right temperature. *–DM-R*

3.3.6 Summary

The activities listed above are expensive and somewhat daunting for a first-time developer, but new biological products regularly pass through these steps with success. Experienced CMOs and testing labs are in place to help novel products and start-up companies reach the clinic. The rewards can be spectacular: biologicals have changed the practice of medicine and the course of many serious diseases. In 2012, six of the nine top-grossing pharmaceuticals were biologicals, with estimated worldwide sales of $44.5 Billion [1]. A number of promising new technologies, such as antibody–drug conjugates, therapeutic and oncolytic vaccines, gene therapy, and regenerative medicines, are also based on biological production. These products will require a similar development effort to establish a solid technical and regulatory foundation and deliver their benefits to patients around the world.

Box 3.12: Resources

1. ICH Quality guidelines (relevant both to US and international regulatory requirements): http://www.ich.org/products/guidelines/quality/article/quality-guidelines.html
2. Points to Consider in the Manufacture and Testing of Monoclonal Antibody Products for Human Use: http://www.fda.gov/downloads/BiologicsBloodVaccines/GuidanceComplianceRegulatoryInformation/OtherRecommendationsforManufacturers/UCM153182.pdf
3. Points to Consider in the Characterization of Cell Lines Used to Produce Biologicals: http://www.fda.gov/downloads/BiologicsBloodVaccines/GuidanceComplianceRegulatoryInformation/OtherRecommendationsforManufacturers/UCM062745.pdf
4. Points to Consider in the Production and Testing of New Drugs and Biologicals Produced by Recombinant DNA Technology: http://www.fda.gov/downloads/BiologicsBloodVaccines/GuidanceComplianceRegulatoryInformation/OtherRecommendationsforManufacturers/UCM062750.pdf

(continued)

Box 3.12 (continued)

5. Points to Consider in the Collection, Processing, and Testing of Ex-Vivo Activated Mononuclear Leukocytes for Administration to Humans: http://www.fda.gov/downloads/BiologicsBloodVaccines/GuidanceComplianceRegulatoryInformation/OtherRecommendationsforManufacturers/UCM062770.pdf
6. Supplement to the Points to Consider in the Production and Testing of New Drugs and Biologic and Produced by Recombinant DNA Technology: Nucleic Acid Characterization and Genetic Stability: http://www.fda.gov/downloads/BiologicsBloodVaccines/GuidanceComplianceRegulatoryInformation/OtherRecommendationsforManufacturers/UCM0 62777.pdf

Table 3.1 Drug substance typical specifications and characterization tests: monoclonal antibody for phase 1 clinical trial

Drug substance in-process tests (performed on clarified harvest where detection is easiest)		
Test	Category	Specification
Bioburden (culture)	Purity	≤5 cfu/mL
Protein A content (ELISA)	Purity	<20 ppm
CHO host cell protein content (ELISA kit)	Purity	<50 ppm
CHO host cell DNA content (PCR)	Purity	10 pg/mg
Mycoplasma detection (culture)	Safety	None detected
Mycobacterium tuberculosis	Safety	None detected
General virus detection by *in vitro* culture	Safety	None detected
General virus detection by *in vivo* culture	Safety	Negative
Specific viruses detection by PCR	Safety	Negative
Drug Substance Specifications		
Endotoxin (limulus amebocyte lysate)	Purity	≤0.5 EU/mL (target depends on patient dose)
Bioburden (culture)	Purity	≤5 cfu/mL
Protein concentration (A_{280} absorbance)	Strength	Target ±5% mg/mL
Cell based bioassay (if available)	Potency	70–130% specific activity versus reference standard
Antibody binding (ELISA)	Identity, potency	Binds to target antigen; 70–130% of reference as potency
Cation exchange chromatography	Identity, Purity	Main peak amount and profile similar to standard
Size exclusion chromatography (HPLC)	Purity	>95% monomer, report percent aggregate
SDS-PAGE (reduced)	Purity	>90 area% of HC plus LC
Isoelectric focusing	Purity	Main peaks match reference profile
pH	General	Target ±0.2 at 25 °C
Osmolality	General	Target ±20% mOsm/kg

Table 3.2 Drug product typical specifications and characterization tests: monoclonal antibody for phase 1 clinical trial

Drug product specifications		
Test	Category	Specification
Sterility	Purity	Meets 21 CFR 610.12
Endotoxin (limulus amebocyte lysate)	Purity	≤0.5 EU/mL (target depends on patient dose)
Appearance	Purity	Clarity and color similar or better than reference standard
Particulate analysis	Purity	Meets US Pharmacopeia requirements
Volume per vial	Strength	Delivers not less than the target volume mL/vial
Protein concentration (A_{280} absorbance)	Strength	Target ±5% mg/mL
Antibody binding (ELISA)	Identity, Potency	Binds to target antigen
Cell based bioassay (if available)	Potency	70–130% specific activity versus reference standard
Cation exchange chromatography	Identity	Main peak amount and profile similar to standard
Size exclusion chromatography (HPLC)	Purity	>95% monomer, report aggregate
SDS-PAGE (native and reduced)	Purity	Profile similar to standard, >90% HC plus LC (reduced)
Isoelectric focusing	Purity	Main peaks match reference profile
pH	General	Target ±0.3 at 25 °C
Osmolality	General	Target ±20% mOsm/kg
Drug product additional characterization tests		
Method	Characteristic	
Peptide map with mass spec	Assess degradation reactions (e.g., deamidation, clips)	
N-terminal sequencing	Matches predicted sequence	
Western blot	Confirm SDS-PAGE bands are antibody derived	
Oligosaccharide mapping	Assess structure and heterogeneity of glycosylation	
Monosaccharide content	Consistency of glycosylation	

3.4 Clinical Trial Design

Ted McCluskey

Once a new agent has been successfully tested in multiple animal models for safety, tolerability, and efficacy, an IND may be filed with the FDA. After the application is accepted, human clinical trials can begin. It can be tempting to rush into testing in humans as quickly as possible. There are, however, several important issues to clinical trial design that bear consideration. This section highlights some of these issues and common pitfalls encountered when conducting clinical research. Because clinical trials involve the safety of human subjects and are so expensive, it is important to plan carefully to avoid costly (both in time and money) trial amendments or discontinuation of the trial.

Box 3.13: Key Terms and Abbreviations

IND: Investigational New Drug application; document filed with the FDA prior to initiating research on human subjects using any drug that has not been previously approved for the proposed clinical indication, dosing regimen, or patient population
FDA: US Food and Drug Administration
Orphan indication: An FDA designation of a disease or condition that affects less than 200,000 people per year in the USA or for a treatment that is not expected to recoup its R&D costs due to pricing constraints
Surrogate endpoint: a biomarker, lab measurement, or imaging test that predicts disease activity and clinical outcome (e.g., ejection fraction via echocardiography, tumor size)
Clinical endpoint: FDA-approved metric of therapeutic success; often something a patient experiences
Placebo effect: when sham treatment results in an improvement in disease
Hawthorne effect: when the act of measuring affects the endpoint's value
Regression to mean: large change away from and eventual return to a baseline measurement
Placebo: sham treatment with inactive compound
IRB: Institutional Review Board; the body regulating the ethics of human clinical research

3.4.1 Pre-IND Meeting

A pre-IND meeting with the FDA can be very valuable as an opportunity to verify all registration requirements and discuss safety considerations or endpoints planned to measure efficacy. Budget enough time into the project timeline to accommodate the FDA-published response time windows. The FDA will expect a pre-IND meeting briefing package submitted 30 days before a scheduled meeting outlining the preclinical work and clinical trial design. When planning a pre-IND meeting, it is best to identify the 4 or 5 key issues that need resolution, suggest the answer that is desired and ask if the FDA agrees. (e.g., "The sponsor believes that three doses can safely be studied in phase 1—Does the Agency agree?") This will prompt clear written answers from the FDA and will hopefully clarify any development questions that the sponsor may have.

3.4.2 Phase 0 Trial

So-called "phase 0" trials are drug-free trials that study patients in the target indication in order to understand the natural disease progression. While not required for all trials, these studies can be very helpful in establishing disease variability between patients and over time. For instance, a phase 0 trial of psoriasis could show that subjects usually seek treatment during a flare up which naturally resolves to baseline over time; using plaque size as an endpoint could overestimate the treatment effect in a short trial. Knowledge of disease variability and progression enables better prediction of the number of patients needed in future trials to detect a desired treatment effect and how long to monitor subjects in order to detect this effect. Sometimes this information is available in published literature, but an orphan indication is unlikely to have much data available. A phase 0 trial is also a good opportunity to test the measurements and tools planned for use in the clinical trial and to verify that the trial sites are adequately trained in the proper use and reporting of both.

Box 3.14: Recommendation

As you transition from animal to human studies, be aware of the use of concomitant medications. These can lead to drug-drug interactions, which may increase or decrease your therapeutic effect or even have a direct impact on your chosen endpoints.

3.4.3 Surrogate and Clinical Endpoints

The endpoints selected to monitor safety and efficacy not only help determine the success of the trial, but also factor in to the duration, cost and site selection for the study. Initial studies often use surrogate endpoints (e.g., changes in biomarkers or imaging studies that predict clinical response) to evaluate efficacy. Surrogate markers may show less variation in the subject pool and a faster response after dosing with drug, making it easier to detect treatment effect in small, short trials. Some surrogate endpoints—for example blood pressure, cholesterol levels, or viral load—are acceptable endpoints for drug registration trials with the FDA, but others are not considered sufficient to validate efficacy and safety because they measure only a small aspect of a complex human disease.

The FDA favors clinical endpoints, things a subject would experience and report, when considering a drug for approval. Clinical endpoints can be "hard" (e.g., death, amputation), adjudicated by an expert panel (e.g., stroke, cancer relapse), biometric (e.g., 6-min walk distance, inspiration volume), validated disease scores (e.g., Unified Parkinson's Disease Rating Scale), or patient response to a questionnaire, such as those used in depression or pain. Clinical endpoints are manifestations of multiple aspects of the disease, and as such they can show a significant variation in the patient population. Because of the variability, clinical endpoints usually require more subjects enrolled to adequately power the study for statistical confidence. It may also take a longer time to detect differences in treatment arms for these metrics.

3.4.4 Importance of Biostatisticians

Just as in preclinical animal studies, it is important to involve biostatisticians in clinical work for advice on trial size, escalation rules, efficacy effect, study power and probability of success. If you can provide data on the natural variation within the collected endpoint and the amount of change you want to detect with a specified confidence, a biostatistician should be able to calculate how many subjects you ought to enroll to "power" your study for those conclusions.

Box 3.15: Recommendation

Be very conservative in projecting clinical event rates for your control arms based on previous studies in your clinical indication. These can change over time and leave your clinical trial underpowered upon completion. For example, rates of death and heart failure from acute myocardial infarction have steadily and markedly declined over the past decade due to advances in therapy.

There are a number of other statistical effects that arise in clinical research. The placebo effect is a perceived or real benefit from a sham treatment. Placebo effects can be marked, prolonged, and even dose-dependent. Sham surgical treatments can also generate placebo effects. The Hawthorne effect occurs when the act of measuring an outcome affects its value. For instance, because he or she knows it will be compared to the baseline walk test, a subject may try to walk farther in a subsequent 6 minute walk test. Lastly, some diseases show a regression to mean, meaning the natural disease progression includes flare up and eventual return to a baseline state. It can be important to account for this, as subjects are more likely to see medical intervention during flare ups. Thus, it is possible to misconstrue a regression to mean as a therapeutic benefit in a small trial.

Box 3.16: Common Pitfalls to Avoid

1. Starting with too high a dose or escalating the dose too quickly early in safety studies.
2. Trying to make efficacy conclusions with an underpowered study.
3. Retroactively looking through subsets of data to try to show efficacy.
4. Trial sites that deviate from the protocol in enrollment criteria, record keeping, or measurements.
5. Poor patient retention and missed follow-up visits.

3.4.5 Trial Design Trends

Over 1993–2004, only around one in five compounds entering phase 1 clinical trials successfully progressed through all clinical trial phases to submit an application to be registered as a new drug with the US FDA [2]. This represents a huge financial loss in R&D expenses. New trials strategies are emerging to improve measurements of efficacy and to "fail fast", that is, rapidly reach go/no-go evaluation points for safety and efficacy.

In adaptive trial design, trial data is periodically unblinded and evaluated for safety and efficacy metrics while the trial is ongoing. This allows for adjustments to enrollment size, assignment to treatment arms, or premature closure of the trial.

Whereas placebos are traditionally the most common type of control for a clinical trial, the use of active controls is growing and will likely increase more in the future (see next section for more discussion of controls). In indications where there is an approved drug on the market, head-to-head comparison with the investigational drug allows direct evaluation of therapeutic benefit. This benefits patients and physicians by assuring that newly approved drugs do in fact provide a benefit over older (possibly generic) drugs. Drug makers were previously reticent to run active control trials for fear their investigational drug would be effective but not more so than previously approved drugs. Recent legislation in the USA aimed at "comparative effectiveness" will likely increase use of active controls.

There are two main types of enrollment strategies. Either you are a "lumper" with broad inclusion criteria for enrollment, or a "splitter" that narrowly defines subject enrollment. Lumpers are focused on maximizing potential market size post drug approval or speeding enrollment rates. Splitters, on the other hand, are worried about variation within the target indication and select for the portion of patients most likely to benefit from the investigational drug. Both enrollment strategies have pros and cons; specific indications may favor one strategy over the other.

3.4.6 *Final Points*

Several important "internal" issues need to be addressed when transitioning into clinical studies. Trial costs must be estimated and internal budget and personnel resources must be planned and accounted for to be able to complete the initial study and all of its follow-up. Considerations for patient enrollment rates at each clinical site can determine the time required to complete the clinical trial. Insurance, Institutional Review Board (IRB) fees and funds for investigator training and auditing must be in place. IRB approval must also be granted at each site before any studies in humans can occur there.

Box 3.17: The Bottom Line

The successful execution on a clinical trial plan requires a team effort and detailed planning. Since it is the most expensive part of drug development, setbacks in execution of clinical trials (e.g., too slow enrollment, shortage of drug, delay in drug arrival to the clinical sites, inappropriate blinding, etc.) can "sink" the program for budgetary reasons rather than because the drug is not effective.

3.5 Overview of Clinical Trials

Ted McCluskey

Before filing the IND, it is important to carefully think through your clinical trial design to minimize risk to test subjects and maximize chances of determining safety and efficacy of your new therapeutic. When a new pharmaceutical entity is tested in humans, the initial trials (phase 1) are designed to be small and focus on safety and tolerability. As more experience is gained, the human trials progress in size and scope (phase 2) and begin to focus on dose and efficacy. With more experience and information on drug dosing in humans, larger confirmatory clinical trials (phase 3) are designed to demonstrate statistically significant safety and efficacy in the target indication.

3.5.1 *Phase 1*

Phase 1 trials are frequently the first time in which a new molecular entity (NME) is to be tested in humans (FIH—"first in human" trial). As such, the goal of the trial is to verify that the safety profile seen in the preclinical animal experience is also applicable to humans. Safety and tolerability are primary concerns and the trial will be limited in size (10–50 subjects). The interaction of the drug with human metabolism will be explored by investigating the pharmacokinetics and pharmacodynamics of the NME in humans. For oral dosing, food effects may also be studied. Phase 1 studies are often done without "blinding" or randomization. Investigators also often include early efficacy readouts, for example a biomarker or enzyme activity, to begin to correlate dosing with therapeutic efficacy.

Box 3.18: Key Terms and Abbreviations

IND: Investigational New Drug application; document filed with the FDA prior to initiating research on human subjects using any drug that has not been previously approved for the proposed clinical indication, dosing regimen, or patient population
NME: New Molecular Entity; a new drug submitted to the FDA Center for Drug Evaluation and Research (CDER)
FIH: "first in human"
Pharmacokinetics: measurements of what the body does to a drug (absorption, distribution, metabolism and excretion)
Pharmacodynamics: measurements of what the drug does to the body (e.g., target off-rate, IC_{50})
Allometric scaling: a method to convert animal dosing to human dosing based on body surface area calculations
SAD: single ascending dose
MAD: multiple ascending dose
CYP: cytochrome P450; enzymes important for metabolizing many drugs
MTD: Maximum tolerated dose
Regimen: the schedule for how much, how often, and under what conditions a drug is administered
Primary endpoint: the measurement used to evaluate trial success, and to which the trial is powered
Secondary endpoints: additional measurements collected during a clinical trial to monitor safety and efficacy; the trial may not be statistically powered to these measurements
Surrogate endpoint: a biomarker, lab measurement, or imaging test that predicts disease activity and clinical outcome (e.g., ejection fraction via echocardiography, tumor size)
Clinical endpoint: FDA-approved metric of therapeutic success; often something a patient experiences
Placebo: sham treatment with inactive compound
Open label trial: unblinded trial with drug only
DSMB: Data Safety Monitoring Board

When there is a reasonable expectation that the new drug will be safe and tolerable, phase 1 trials are commonly performed in healthy (often male) volunteers. Phase 1 trials are normally conducted in specialized phase 1 trial units where subjects can be carefully monitored for adverse events and timed blood samples (or other measurements) may be obtained. When the new agent carries significant expectation of toxicity, as in the case of chemotherapeutic agents or agents designed to treat patients with an acute illness such as myocardial infarction, the trial may be performed in subjects who have the disease. These trials are sometimes referred to as "phase 1/2."

The phase 1 trial will typically start with a dose expected, based on allometric scaling from preclinical animal studies, to have no effect in humans (The FDA has provided a guidance document on selection of initial dose based upon the highest nontoxic animal dose [3]). The dose is then escalated until physiological effects occur. In a Single Ascending Dose (SAD) trial, subjects are given a single dose and data/samples are collected typically for >5 half-lives. In Multiple Ascending Dose trials (MAD), subjects receive repeat doses (e.g., one pill every 6 h) and the pharmacokinetics of increasing drug levels are observed. In both SAD and MAD, new subject groups are dosed at higher levels until lack of tolerability occurs (or a full therapeutic effect is noted). For a more extensive description of a widely used dose escalation procedure, see the description by Rubinstein and Simon [4].

After the first phase 1 SAD and MAD trials give an initial readout of safety, additional phase 1 studies are often run to look at: drug-drug interactions, if other medications are frequently co-administered in this indication; CYP inhibition, if metabolism is important for drug elimination; and food interactions, if the drug is administered orally. These trials will look for factors that alter the investigational drug pharmacokinetics and may change the safety profile in a subset of patients. Knowledge gained here may lead to changes in clinical trial design and/or exclude certain subjects from larger phase 2 and 3 efficacy trials.

At the end of the phase 1 trials, the investigations should have established the range of safe doses and a maximum tolerated dose (MTD). Also, the pharmacokinetics (absorption, distribution, metabolism and excretion) should be known and an acceptable route of administration established. The dose limiting toxicity should be identified and there may be some indication of the anticipated therapeutic effect or a desired effect upon an early efficacy surrogate marker.

3.5.2 Phase 2

The goal of the phase 2 trial(s) is to establish the conditions (final dose, route, regimen) and the endpoints (primary, secondary and surrogate) that will be used in the phase 3 confirmatory trials, as well as to continue to build the drug safety profile.

Because the phase 1 trials have established some level of safety and tolerability, the phase 2 studies will usually be larger (50–250 subjects). Phase 2 trials study a range of doses and/or dosing regimens in subjects with the targeted indication. A typical dose range will start with a very-low dose and progress to a low, medium and high dose; with the separation between doses dependent on the safe range observed in phase 1. Often surrogate endpoints (a clinical measurement or a lab value, such as a decrease in a biomarker or an angiographic appearance) will be used to measure the therapeutic effect of different doses of medication. A further distinction is sometimes drawn between a phase 2a trial that studies dose and regimen selection to determine the MTD and a phase 2b trial that focuses on measures of efficacy to find the minimally effective dose.

Box 3.19: What Surprised an Academician?

When we visited one of the clinical sites that was recruited to our phase 2a clinical trial, it became evident why there was such a great difference between the promised enrollment rate to our trial (10 patients a month) and the actual rate (1 patient in 2 months). The nurse coordinator's office had binders for three other trials from other companies that focused on the same patient population. I learned to ask about other ongoing trials in the same indication at the site, in addition to asking how many patients the site sees that fit the inclusion criteria for our trial. *–DM-R*

Phase 2 trials are often conducted as randomized, controlled, and blinded studies. There are several types of controls investigators can use. The most common is a placebo control, where the inactive compound looks, smells, tastes and is administered like the real drug. Other designs include randomized open, used to compare things like surgical intervention to drugs; active controls (e.g., another drug approved for the target indication); historical patient data; or as an add-on to standard treatment. For a repurposing effort, investigators will occasionally run a single-arm open label trial, which only treats with active drug.

When there are multiple treatment arms (control plus one or more active doses or regimens), the trial can be designed with parallel or crossover treatment arms. In a parallel study, the subject receives the same treatment (active or control) for the full time course of the study. A popular crossover design has a "wash in" period where subjects are monitored untreated for a period of time, then randomized to a control or active treatment arm. After a specified treatment duration, subjects are switched from active to control and vice versa, with an optional "wash out" period of no treatment between the conversion if the drug is long-acting. This study design is very statistically robust because each subject serves as his or her own control.

Blinding is very important in clinical trial design: not only to prevent investigator conflicts of interest from influencing data analysis, but also to properly measure any placebo effect subjects experience. Phase 2 studies can be single blinded (subject does not know whether receiving active or control), double blinded (subject and trial staff do not know), or triple blinded (subject, staff, trial sponsor, and core lab do not know). Blinding the core lab responsible for taking and assessing surrogate endpoints further validates the independence of the clinical trial findings. In triple blinded studies, set up a data safety monitoring board (DSMB) to remain unblinded to direct investigators how to respond to any adverse events that arise in the trial.

The size of a phase 2 trial should be determined by the number of subjects that will be needed to adequately 'power' the trial to be able to observe a statistically meaningful change in the target surrogate marker. Simple calculators are available online (http://www.epibiostat.ucsf.edu/biostat/sampsize.html), but it is strongly advised to consult an experienced clinical trial biostatistician for a final trial size determination. The biostatistician will ask the clinician: "What is the smallest change in a trial endpoint that you want to be able to detect?" and from this information and published values of the surrogate endpoint in the target population, the biostatistician should be able to provide the number of subjects needed to treat to be able to detect the desired change in the surrogate.

Endpoints in phase 2 trials are chosen to monitor safety, detect lack of tolerability, and show evidence of efficacy using surrogate and clinical endpoints. Clinical endpoints are things the subject notices or reports to a doctor, and the FDA favors these measures of therapeutic efficacy for registrational trials (with some exceptions). Surrogate endpoints, however, may show less variability or respond more rapidly to treatment. For example, following all subjects until death to show an increased survival rate takes much longer than measuring heart function with an echocardiogram after heart attack. Often the surrogate endpoint is chosen as the primary endpoint in phase 2 (and the trial is 'powered' on this endpoint) and the phase 3 clinical endpoint is measured but is listed as a secondary endpoint (since it is likely to be 'underpowered' with the smaller size of the phase 2 trial).

Box 3.20: Recommendation

Picking the wrong clinical or surrogate endpoints can obscure a true therapeutic effect or drastically increase the time and cost of running a clinical trial. Consult FDA guidance and past clinical trials in your indication (or a related indication) to see what metrics others have used.

It is important that the techniques for assessing the clinical outcome in phase 3 be clearly established and rehearsed at each trial site during phase 2, so that there are no interruptions for protocol amendments in phase 3. A successful phase 2 program will help minimize "surprises" in clinical operations and trial conduct that may occur during the phase 3 program. Phase 2 programs are where most programs falter, with the percent of programs successfully transitioning from phase 1 to phase 3 having recently dropped from 28% (2006–2007) to 18% (2008–2009) [5].

3.5.3 *Phase 3*

At the end of successful phase 1 and 2 trials, the new therapeutic agent should have a reasonable level of assurance of safety and some measures of efficacy based on surrogate endpoints. The trials, however, have likely been underpowered to show efficacy on a clinical endpoint with statistical confidence. Before registering a new drug, the FDA requires two phase 3 trials large enough to show safety and efficacy via an approved clinical endpoint with statistical confidence $p<0.05$. Occasionally, after discussion with the FDA, treatments for serious medical conditions are approved after a single phase 3 trial with an even lower p-value. Unfortunately, only when these significantly larger subject groups are studied can unsuspected safety issues be discovered and true clinical efficacy be proven.

References

1. Compiled from web: http://www.fiercepharma.com/special-reports/15-best-selling-drugs-2012
2. DiMasi JA, Feldman L, Seckler A, Wilson A (2010) Pharmaceutical innovation in the 21st century: new drug approvals in the first decade, 2000–2009. Clin Pharmacol Ther 87:272–277
3. FDA guidance: estimating the maximum safe starting dose in initial clinical trials for therapeutics in adult healthy volunteers (http://www.fda.gov/downloads/Drugs/Guidances/UCM078932.pdf)
4. Rubinstein LV, Simon RM. Phase I Clinical Trial Design, National Cancer Institute (http://linus.nci.nih.gov/techreport/phaseIctd.pdf)
5. Arrowsmith J (2011) Trial watch: phase II failures: 2008–2010. Nat Rev Drug Discov 10:328–329

Chapter 4
Transferring Technology

Daria Mochly-Rosen and Kevin Grimes

Most academic institutions require their researchers and clinicians to assign all intellectual property rights to the institution. The university technology transfer office (TTO) then becomes the clearinghouse for filing patents and granting licenses for new inventions. Navigating this process is usually fairly straightforward, with a few important caveats to note. First, it is of upmost importance that we protect the intellectual property that our research generates by disclosing discoveries to the university TTO so that they can assess the invention for patentability. Unless a patent is filed before public disclosure (e.g., publications, abstracts, public presentations at scientific meetings), the invention is no longer patentable throughout most of the world. Without patent protection, it will be impossible for a company to recoup the considerable costs of developing a new drug. Second, we must ensure that interactions with the for-profit industrial sector (e.g., consulting, holding options/stock in a company) do not interfere with our academic mission to research, mentoring and administrative university responsibilities. Managing conflicts of interest is essential to maintain an independent, unbiased environment in academia, and most institutions have clearly delineated policies. This chapter provides an introduction to intellectual property, working with university TTOs, and avoiding conflicts of interest.

D. Mochly-Rosen (✉)
Chemical and Systems Biology, Stanford University School of Medicine, 269 Campus Drive, Center for Clinical Science Research Rm 3145a, Stanford, CA 94305-5174, USA
e-mail: sparkmed@stanford.edu

K. Grimes
Chemical and Systems Biology, Stanford University School of Medicine, 269 Campus Drive, Center for Clinical Science Research Rm 3145c, Stanford, CA 94305-5174, USA
e-mail: kgrimes@stanford.edu

D. Mochly-Rosen and K. Grimes (eds.), *A Practical Guide to Drug Development in Academia*, SpringerBriefs in Pharmaceutical Science & Drug Development, DOI 10.1007/978-3-319-02201-7_4,

4.1 Intellectual Property

Judy Mohr

Like them or not, patents are a necessary part of the pharmaceutical business. Because of the high development costs incurred in obtaining regulatory approval to market a pharmaceutical product, potential corporate partners and investors insist that the product be protected by one or more patents with sufficient patent term remaining after product launch to have an exclusive market position to recoup the development costs. Further, the generic drug industry is sophisticated and is rapidly able to manufacture a bioequivalent product of identical composition to a branded product and, likely, a bioequivalent product that differs sufficiently in composition to avoid patent claims covering the product. Thus, a company developing a pharmaceutical product—whether as a new molecular entity (NME), a new delivery vehicle/platform for a previously approved drug, or a new method of treatment using an already approved compound—must define a patent strategy that supports its own business objectives, yet is also mindful of the inevitable generic competition to the pharmaceutical product. This section touches on three important aspects in building any patent portfolio: the effect of publicly disclosing the invention before filing for patent protection, patent searching to assess patentability of an invention, and freedom to operate.

Box 4.1: Key Terms and Abbreviations

NME: New Molecular Entity; a new drug submitted to the FDA Center for Drug Evaluation and Research (CDER)
USPTO: US Patent and Trademark Office
PCT: Patent Cooperation Treaty
FTO: Freedom to Operate
IND: Investigational New Drug application; document filed with the FDA prior to initiating research on human subjects using any drug that has not been previously approved for the proposed clinical indication, dosing regimen, or patient population

4.1.1 Public Disclosure and Patent Filing

In order for an invention to be patentable, it must be "novel and non-obvious" as defined in the patent law. This novelty requirement states that an invention cannot be patented if certain public disclosures of the invention have been made. An important aspect of the novelty rule in the USA is that an invention will not be patentable if:

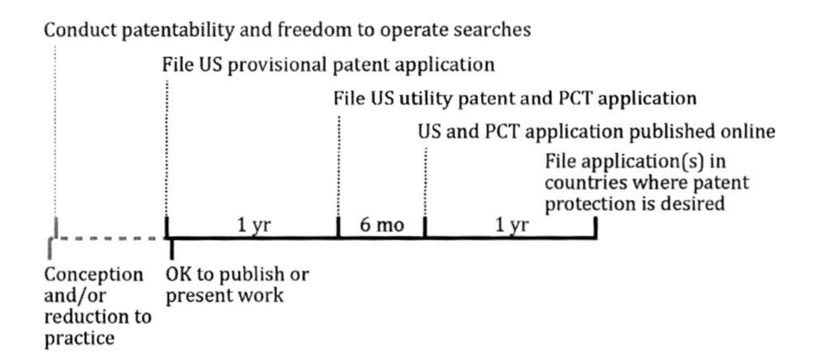

Fig. 4.1 Patent filing timeline

- The invention was described in a publication more than 1 year prior to the filing date.
- The invention was used publicly, or offered for sale to the public more than 1 year prior to the filing date.

The takeaway message from these rules is that in the USA there is a 1-year period after the first public disclosure or offer for sale of an invention during which a patent application must be filed (Fig. 4.1). This 1-year period is unforgiving, which means that an inventor who does not file for patent protection on her new invention within this grace period will lose all rights in the USA to obtain patent protection on the invention. In some cases, simply explaining the invention to friends and coworkers without any obligation of confidentiality may have started the "ticking" of this 1-year clock.

Most other countries do not grant any grace period between public disclosure and patent filing. Therefore, it is almost always preferable to file a patent application before any public disclosure of the invention, particularly for pharmaceuticals for which worldwide market potential is desirable. Public disclosure includes publishing your invention in a journal or presenting your work at a conference or talk.

4.1.2 Patent Searching to Assess Patentability

A first step in determining a patent strategy for any new product is to know the "lay of the land," as it were, of publications related to the product. This is a critical step in determining whether your invention is novel and non-obvious—two essential requirements for patentability. Your publication search should include both the scientific literature and the patent literature. Prior to beginning a search, make a list of the new product's components and draft the proposed product label regarding how the product will be used (i.e., the disease or condition for which FDA approval of the product will be sought and how it will be dosed). This information should track closely, if not identically, with the contents of any drafted or filed regulatory documents (e.g., IND). Knowing the product components and the intended label use identifies some key words for initial searching of the patent literature (issued patents and published applications) and the scientific literature, to obtain a solid understanding of prior publications related to the product.

Box 4.2: What Surprised an Academician?

If you want to be sure that your invention will never benefit patients, publish your idea and data before filing a patent. Exclusive and preferably worldwide intellectual property rights are essential to recoup the huge development costs of new drugs and biologics; without IP protection, no one will develop your drug.—*DM-R*

Unless you have some familiarity with patents or patent searching, it may be easier to start searching in the scientific literature. Search terms identified using the approach above can be searched in on-line databases, such as Pubmed and Google® Scholar. From the search of the scientific literature, the authors and/or institutions (academic or commercial) of the most relevant articles should be added to the list of search terms for searching the patent databases.

A search of issued patents and published patent applications is best done using a combination of several databases. Patents are jurisdictional, so it is necessary to search both US and international databases to identify patent publications that may be relevant to patentability. Examination of the following three databases will give a fairly thorough search:

1. US Patent and Trademark Office (USPTO): http://www.uspto.gov

   The Web site of the US Patent Office contains a database of the full text of granted US patents from 1976 to the present, and a separate database of all published US patent applications. Both databases should be searched, and the search interface for both has quick and advanced searching options. The search results are hyperlinked to the relevant documents, making it easy to review them. Other Web sites can also be used to download the text of granted patents and published applications in the familiar two column format, such as www.patentfetcher.com or www.pat2pdf.com.
2. Espacenet.com: http://worldwide.espacenet.com

   This database permits searching of European patents and applications, and using the "advanced search" tab, it can be searched by title, inventor, applicant (company name), etc. This database also has a tool, INPADOC (*in*ternational *pa*tent *doc*uments) that will identify all counterpart patents and applications, or "family members," of a relevant patent or application. For example, if your search identifies a US patent of interest, enter the US patent number in the "publication number" search field on the advanced search page, click on the result, then look for the "View INPADOC patent family" link and click on it to see whether the US patent has counterpart filings outside the USA.
3. World Intellectual Property Organization (WIPO) PatentScope: http://www.wipo.int/patentscope/search/en/search.jsf

This database is maintained by WIPO and allows a search of PCT (Patent Cooperation Treaty) applications for international filings. Both simple and "structured" (advanced) search options are available for more than a million international patent applications. The results from a search of the databases are then reviewed to identify documents that describe in whole or in part the invention.

4.1.3 Patent Searching to Assess Freedom to Operate

"Freedom to operate," abbreviated "FTO," refers to whether a particular action, such as testing or commercializing a product, can be done without infringing the valid granted patent rights of another party. Since patent rights are jurisdictional, an FTO analysis needs to be done in each particular country where the product is to be manufactured or sold.

The USPTO and espacenet patent search sites noted above are equally useful for searching for patents potentially relevant to FTO. A key difference between assessing patentability and assessing FTO is that the latter needs only focus on the *claims* of *granted* patents, whereas the former must consider the disclosure of the entire patent document.

If searching identifies a claim in a granted patent that may be relevant to FTO, further investigation is needed to ascertain whether it poses an actual barrier to commercializing the product. For example, words in a patent claim may be subject to definitions in the patent specification, the legal term for the introductory text, and alter the scope of the patent claim; or admissions may have been made by the patentee while the patent application was being examined that narrow the meaning of claim terms. Also, fees are required to maintain patents in force and if the patent owner has not timely paid the fees, the patent may no longer be enforceable. Advice of a patent attorney is typically required to advise regarding the legal scope of patent claims.

4.2 Working with the University Technology Transfer Office

Katharine Ku

Because academic faculty are some of the most creative people in the world, universities have established mechanisms to try to bring their inventions to the marketplace.

4.2.1 What is TTO?

University technology licensing, often referred to as "technology transfer," is the formal mechanism whereby the university transfers intellectual property to outside entities through a licensing agreement. Most universities in the USA (and many universities outside the USA) have a patent policy that requires inventors to assign intellectual property rights to their university if the invention was created using university resources. These universities also have a technology transfer office (TTO) whose mission is to promote the transfer of university-generated technologies to industry for society's use and benefit, a mission that fits right into translational research. Universities also often have royalty-sharing policies that provide that a share of royalty income, if any, goes to the inventors.

Box 4.3: Key Terms and Abbreviations

TTO: Technology transfer office; the university group responsible for managing intellectual property owned by the university
License: a legal agreement granting another party rights to use intellectual property
Licensee: third party paying for access to technology
Royalty: payment based on revenue generated from licensed technology
Option: a legal agreement granting temporary rights to intellectual property

4.2.2 Licensing Intellectual Property

The path of an invention moving from the laboratory to marketplace is rarely swift. Once an invention disclosure is filed with the technology licensing office, a licensing professional will review the invention with inventors to learn about potential applications. The office will develop a licensing strategy: they will evaluate the invention by considering the technical and market risks, decide whether to patent the invention, actively market the invention to companies that might be interested in the invention, and seek a product champion within a company before negotiating a licensing agreement. The goal is to find the best company or companies to develop and commercialize a technology.

Licensing and commercialization do not follow a set timetable. Because most university-originated inventions are quite early-stage, it may take years before a product is commercially developed. In fact, it is rare to have an invention make genuinely significant royalties, although many inventions generate modest royalties. Approximately two-thirds of all university inventions are never licensed. The likelihood of finding a licensee will depend on the development stage of the technology, the market, competing technologies, and the resources required to bring a new concept to the marketplace.

Box 4.4: What Surprised an Academician?

Because the TTO is sensitive to the academic mission to share knowledge, filing for a patent rarely slows down publication, submission of an abstract, or giving a talk. Filing a disclosure with the TTO can be as simple as attaching your planned talk or draft manuscript to get the process going.—*DM-R*

A license grant may be nonexclusive, which gives several companies the right to develop products based on the technology; nonexclusive licenses often are used to license transgenic mice, biological material, screening assays, methods of making recombinant molecules, research tools, etc. Alternatively, if a technology requires significant investment of resources before a product can be introduced into the marketplace, an exclusive license to one company may be appropriate, as is the case for most drug or device inventions. The licensee (i.e., company who licenses the technology) may be an established company or a new business start-up. Licenses typically include terms that require the licensee to meet certain performance requirements (also known as diligence requirements) and to make financial payments to the university. These financial payments often include: an upfront or signing fee (similar to a down payment), annual fees to maintain the license, milestone payments if certain development goals are met, and earned royalties based on a percentage of the revenue generated by product sales. If the licensee is a start-up company, the university often receives equity in the company as part of the licensing agreement. Sometimes there are "field of use" restrictions in licenses—e.g., research-only license, diagnostic products, therapeutic products, etc.

As an initial step, a company may request an option agreement from the TTO. This allows the company to evaluate the technology for a limited time before a formal license agreement is concluded. Typically, the agreement lasts for 6–12 months in return for a modest option fee.

A typical successful license agreement lasts for many years, as long as 20 or more years. The original agreement is often renegotiated because unforeseen market and technical conditions have changed.

4.2.3 *Patent Cost and Time to Issue*

Many inventors are focused on "patent protection," not realizing that it often takes 4–5 years for a patent to issue and that one patent filing and prosecution can be expensive, costing more than $40–50,000 per patent. Because of the expense, licensing offices need to be very judicious in choosing whether to file a patent application on a particular invention. Sometimes the office will conduct a patentability analysis—a prior art search to compare the invention to previously issued patents and publications related to the invention—before deciding to file. Licensing offices must receive an invention disclosure and decide whether to file a patent *before* an invention is described in a publication or public presentation because such public disclosures will preclude patenting.

4.2.4 Conflict of Interest

Conflict of interest is inherent in technology transfer if the inventors are actively involved with the licensee in the development of the technology. Nonetheless, technology transfer can be more effective if the inventors are involved as consultants or founders of companies. Licensing to a faculty-associated start-up can often be the most effective way to transfer early-stage technology, because existing companies are reluctant to take the risks involved in developing unproven technology. To manage conflicts of interest, most universities have a conflict of interest disclosure and review process, with the main concerns involving separation of research at the university from that of the company and ensuring that students are not affected by a faculty's financial interest/consulting arrangements.

Consulting agreements are considered to be personal agreements between a company and a researcher. Although each university is different with respect to prior review, consulting arrangements are often not negotiated or reviewed by the university. Researchers who enter into consulting agreements should be familiar with their university's policies relevant to consulting activities. The researcher is generally expected to ensure that the terms of the consulting arrangement are consistent with university policies, including those related to intellectual property ownership, employment responsibilities, and disclosure of industry relationships.

Box 4.5: The Bottom Line

Technology transfer is an essential means to the commercialization of discoveries and inventions from academia. The process can be complex and requires juggling the interests of numerous constituents, including inventors, licensees, the university, the government and the public. The end result can be satisfying to all parties when university technology is successfully translated to industry for society's benefit.

4.3 Avoiding Conflicts of Interest

Emily Egeler

As university faculty members get more involved in the drug development process, it is essential that academic institutions maintain their high-quality unbiased research and education missions. This is their responsibility to their students, the government agencies and the public who fund the research, and ultimately to the patients who are treated by these new therapeutics. The potential for conflicts of interest is common and sometimes unavoidable as academic researchers and clinicians try to translate their discoveries. The goal should not be to shun all interactions with for-profit entities, but rather to manage and report these interactions in a transparent way to protect the public.

Box 4.6: What Surprised an Academician?

It is not against most university and funding agency policies for academics to financially benefit from their research and clinical work. On the contrary, institutions should encourage faculty to work long and hard to make new therapeutics a reality. It is, however, essential that the public trust the impartiality of the research and clinical trial data generated in publically funded institutions and that the independence of trainee education and mentorship be maintained. This is why it is so important to properly disclose conflicts of interest.—*DM-R*

4.3.1 Identifying Conflicts of Interest

The Sunshine Act went into effective March 31, 2013 as part of the *Patient Protection Affordable Care Act*, which elicits transparency of physician payments or ownership interests made by all pharmaceutical, medical device, biotechnology, and medical supply manufacturers doing business in the USA. Due to this new law, many research institutions and funding agencies now publically report conflicts of interest for affiliated researchers—sometimes under the less pejorative "Industry Affiliations" heading. It is often, however, left to the individual researcher to ensure the accuracy of this reporting. Each institution will have their own policies for internal reporting of conflicts of interest (COI) and determining if the relationship is a significant financial interest worthy of reporting. Currently, the Public Health Service, which encompasses many federal agencies including the NIH, FDA and CDC, defines a significant financial relationship as (a) income greater than $5,000 per year, (b) equity or ownership in a non-publically traded company, or (c) personal income from intellectual property outside of your university royalties.

The simplest rule of thumb for identifying COI is to consider how a patient would feel to first learn about an industry relationship from a news report. If a reasonable person might conclude that relationships or interests could influence academic responsibilities, investigators should disclose the COI following the university's protocols. Reporting a conflict of interest does not imply that the research or clinical work is actually biased; maintaining integrity of research findings is still a personal responsibility. Instead, reporting conflicts of interest is an avenue to increase transparency to the public between funding and clinical outcomes in drug development. Managing a COI may be as simple as adding a notification statement to an informed consent form, but some COIs will prevent participation in running or analyzing a clinical trial.

Box 4.7: Guide to Identifying Conflicts of Interest

1. Do any financial interests or relationships, including things without current value like stock options, relate directly to my responsibilities and role as an academic investigator?
2. Could my research findings impact the success of these interests, or appear to affect the success?
3. Could a reasonable person conclude that my research or role at the university might be influenced by my financial ties?
4. Does my institution have requirements to report interests for spouses, partners or children?

Box 4.8: What Surprised an Academician?

Some universities require us to report financial conflicts of interest for our spouse, partner or dependents in addition to our own industry connections. Usually this is only necessary if their connections relate to our area of research or clinical practice.—*DM-R*

4.3.2 Conflicts of Interest to Avoid

Some industry relationships are never appropriate. Most importantly, clinicians should never be involved in a clinical trial in which they stand to financially benefit from the outcome. Industry connections should also not influence treatment selection in patient care. For instance, clinicians cannot accept company payment for each patient they enroll in a clinical trial. On the research side, it is important that academics keep their university role and responsibilities separate from any for-profit ventures. For instance, graduate students or postdoctoral scholars should not be coerced into acting as employees for a start-up company or have their research topic areas restricted. An academic researcher should not accept corporate funding or in kind gifts that require a delay in publication, restrict research to specific topics of corporate interest, or use university resources to preferentially benefit a particular company.

4.3.3 *Managing Conflicts of Interest: Clinicians*

Disclosing conflicts of interest in the clinical care setting is intended to solidify public confidence in the results of clinical trials and to ensure that clinicians are acting in the best interest of their patients. Areas of concern include intentional or, more likely, unconscious bias in interpretation of study results, reporting of adverse events, or selection of a course of treatment. Accepting gifts from companies, including things like free drug samples or even pens with the company logo, is not allowed in some universities as it is seen to influence the open, independent environment of the academic institution or affect their tax-exempt status.

That being said, clinicians should be able to partner with industry to improve patient care. It is important to be aware of university policies and avoid situations that impact the impartiality of the study design, data collection, or findings. Expect to disclose conflicts of interest for any human subject research protocol submission to the Institutional Review Board, grant application, or Material and Human Tissue Transfer Agreements. Institutional COI refers to any connections to specific companies at the university or hospital level. Site selection for a clinical trial is usually the only instance that is impacted by institutional COI. A hospital or academic medical center may decline to participate as a clinical site if the institution would benefit financially from positive study results.

4.3.4 *Managing Conflicts of Interest: Researchers (M.D. or Ph.D.)*

The public relies on researchers from universities and other academic institutions to be impartial and comprehensive when reporting their findings. Not only is the public the end recipient of any drugs developed based on the research, but they are also the sponsor of research supported by federal grants. The most common financial conflicts of interest for researchers arise from paid consulting, accepting monetary or in kind support from an industry partner, or having equity ownership in a start-up company that holds intellectual property licenses from the university.

It is important that financial ties do not affect or appear to affect the design, conduct, interpretation or reporting of our research. Nor should industry affiliations interfere with the selection of research topics. Importantly, we must also protect the integrity of our educational mission. Our teaching and mentorship must not be biased by financial considerations. Agreements cannot restrict students' ability to publish or present results, and trainee work should be independent from any mentoring faculty's COI. Within the academic setting, all meetings should be educational and not for marketing purposes.

Box 4.9: The Bottom Line

Conflicts of interest include any industry connections that could appear to influence the design, conduct or interpretation of research or clinical trials. Reporting a COI does not imply that the results are definitely biased. Accurate disclosure of a COI is essential to maintain transparency and public trust in research. Consult university policies for specific guidance on what and how to report.

4.4 Working with the University Compliance Office

Jennifer Swanton Brown, Nicholas Gaich, and Steven Alexander

This section focuses on academic institutional requirements for conducting human research, using Stanford University as the specific example. While each institution's compliance infrastructure and policies will vary to some degree, the guiding principles are the same: to protect human research subjects; to ensure high quality design and execution of research protocols; and to ensure that government regulatory requirements are met.

Box 4.10: Key Terms and Abbreviations

HRPP: Human Research Protection Plan; a collection of policies, guidances, and supporting documents governing human subject research and the protection of participants http://humansubjects.stanford.edu/hrpp/manual.html#hrpp
RPH: Research Policy Handbook; Stanford policies regarding the conduct of research http://rph.stanford.edu/index.html
CFR: Code of Federal Regulations; rules and regulations published in the Federal register by the executive departments and agencies of the Federal Government of the USA
RAC: Risk Assessment Committee; a multidisciplinary panel that evaluates studies for financial or administrative risks and evaluates requests to waive a policy related to administration of clinical trial operations. RAC provides an additional vehicle for risk analysis, but does not evaluate human subject protections or scientific validity
IND: Investigational New Drug application; document filed with the FDA prior to initiating research on human subjects using any drug that has not been previously approved for the proposed clinical indication, dosing regimen, or patient population
HIPAA: Health Insurance Portability and Accountability Act of 1996

Regulatory compliance at Stanford for research involving human subjects is *defined* in the Human Research Protection Program (HRPP) and *administered* by the Research Compliance Office (RCO) in the Office of the Vice Provost and Dean of Research. The RCO administers Stanford's eight Administrative Panels for Human Subjects in Research, the formal name for the Stanford Institutional Review Board (IRB). Additionally, and based on allocation of funding for an investigator-initiated project, there may be University sponsored project and research compliance requirements administered by the School of Medicine's Research Management Group (RMG).

Box 4.11: Key Departments

IRB (Institutional Review Board) is the committee formally designated by an institution to review, approve the initiation of, and to conduct periodic review of biomedical research involving human subjects (21 CFR 56.102(g)) http://humansubjects.stanford.edu/

RCO (Research Compliance Office) supports the Stanford Administrative Panels for Research Compliance, which report to the President through the Office of the Vice Provost and Dean of Research http://researchcompliance.stanford.edu/

RMG (Research Management Group) facilitates research in the School of Medicine, serving as the institutional representative and expert partner on research administration providing support and oversight of sponsored projects http://med.stanford.edu/rmg/

OSR (Office of Sponsored Research) provides service and administrative expertise to the University research community and represents the interests of the Board of Trustees of the Leland Stanford Junior University in its contractual relationships with external sponsors, except for industry-funded clinical trials, which are handled by RMG http://ora.stanford.edu/ora/osr/default.asp

Spectrum OTC is the Operations, Training and Compliance component of Spectrum, the Stanford Center for Clinical and Translational Education and Research

CCTO (Cancer Clinical Trials Office) provides regulatory, administrative, research, and educational services to Cancer Institute investigators conducting clinical trials

For industry-funded clinical trials, a Stanford investigator may initiate all three phases of research oversight in parallel: IRB (human subjects) approval, contract negotiation, and budget development. IRB approval is required for all human subject research and is not contingent on the other two processes. Detailed budgets are required for sponsored projects and strongly encouraged for department-funded projects. Contracts are contingent on meeting all sponsored project compliance requirements and IRB approval, and are needed if drug, device, biologic, or funding is received from, or data, publication rights, or intellectual property is shared with an entity outside Stanford, for example from an industry collaborator or as a sub-award from another academic institution.

4.4.1 IND Requirements

An Investigational New Drug application (IND) must be filed with the FDA before any unapproved drug can be used in research with human subjects in the USA. The Stanford IRB will require written evidence of FDA concurrence with the IND if the compound being studied has never received FDA approval for any use in the USA.

If the drug being studied has prior approval by the FDA for use in the USA, the study may require a new IND or be IND-exempt. Stanford's IRB application walks the investigator through the regulatory questions that assist an investigator in making this determination. Clinical trials are typically IND exempt if the researcher studies the drug according to its legally marketed labeling. Trials typically require a new IND if the research involves a "route of administration or dosage level or use in a patient population or other factor *that significantly increases the risks* (or decreases the acceptability of the risks) associated with the use of the drug product" (21 CFR 312.2(b)(iii)).

Box 4.12: Recommendation

Spectrum Study Navigator is a Web site dashboard where Stanford investigators can store and access all essential study information in one shared, easy-to-use interface. The investigator can also access project support services (e.g., statistical consultations), post remarks for team members, and upload and manage study documents. https://spectrum/studynavigator/

4.4.2 IRB Oversight

Applications to the IRB are submitted via an electronic submission process, called eProtocol. For studies that are not IND-exempt, the IRB requires documentation of a FDA approved IND. Acceptable documentation includes a letter issued by the FDA indicating the IND number.

Informed Consent templates are available from the IRB Web site. The investigator needs to make sure to provide any advertisements or recruitment materials to the IRB at the time of application. Guidance on Data and Safety Monitoring or special regulations for research with children is also available among the IRB's comprehensive guidance documents. By carefully following the Informed Consent templates and fully answering the eProtocol questions prior to IRB application submission, a researcher can expect an approval from the IRB within 4–6 weeks. The Stanford IRB also reviews and approves Health Insurance Portability and Accountability Act of 1996 (HIPAA) authorizations for research.

There are additional requirements and approvals for research conducted at the Veterans Administration Palo Alto Health Care System (VAPAHCS) or the Clinical and Translational Research Unit (CTRU). Cancer-related research may also require review by the Stanford Cancer Institute's Scientific Review Committee (SRC). When required, reviews by the Stanford Stem Cell Research Oversight (SCRO) committee and/or Administrative Panel on Biosafety (APB) are coordinated by the Research Compliance Office.

4.4.3 Sponsor–Investigator Research Training and Support

Sponsor–investigator research (SIR) is defined as a research conducted by a Stanford investigator who holds an IND from the FDA. The Stanford IRB requires protocol-specific sponsor–investigator research training for the Principal Investigator (and/or Protocol Director) and research team prior to initial IRB approval. This training is provided by regulatory staff from the Cancer Clinical Trials Office (CCTO) or Study Facilitators from Spectrum Operations, Training and Compliance. Training includes review of required regulatory documentation and reporting to the FDA and IRB. Prior to continuing approval of an ongoing project, RCO requires a compliance review, conducted by compliance analysts from RCO or by representatives of the Stanford Cancer Institute Data and Safety Monitoring Committee (DSMC). Sample training and review documents can be found on the IRB Web site.

Training and study facilitation are available for any aspect of investigator-initiated research.

- Sample templates, logs, and standard operating procedures (SOPs) are available through CCTO and Spectrum OTC.
- Good Clinical Practice training is available upon request or when required.
- Spectrum OTC provides Study Facilitators who guide investigators and study personnel through the clinical research process, from study idea and design through close-out and publication, for clinical and translational research projects. Study Facilitators are health professionals with extensive clinical research experience and expertise in navigating the Stanford clinical and translational research system. https://spectrum/accordions/operations-training-and-compliance/?ch2=1
- CCTO regulatory staff assist with IND applications and amendments for submission to the FDA, study initiation, processing and tracking safety reports, regulatory documentation and IRB, SRC and CTRU submissions. http://cancer.stanford.edu/trials/contact_us/regulatory_staff.html

- In the event of a regulatory audit, staff from Spectrum OTC and CCTO can coordinate with auditors and the IRB, review study documentation prior to the audit, and provide expert advice.

4.4.4 RAC Review

Stanford policy requires industry sponsors to provide insurance for potential research-related injury during clinical trials. However, many industry sponsors are reluctant to provide insurance coverage when a Stanford researcher is conducting investigator-initiated research with an approved drug. In such cases, a waiver of this policy may be obtained by appeal to the Risk Assessment Committee (RAC). Application to this committee is initiated by a Stanford contract officer or a Spectrum Study Facilitator. RAC approval is required prior to completion of the contract.

4.4.5 ClinicalTrials.gov Registration

With the exception of phase 1 clinical trials, any study conducted with an IND requires registration with the ClinicalTrials.gov public registry. Registration must be completed prior to first patient enrollment. The IRB application triggers this process and guidance documents are available on the Spectrum OTC Web site. Generally the principal investigator is responsible for registering his/her study and for meeting all the requirements of ClinicalTrials.gov registration, including uploading of study results.

Box 4.13: Required Training

CITI (Collaborative Institutional Training Initiative) is the online training tutorial required of all personnel conducting research with human subjects. http://humansubjects.stanford.edu/resources/req_tutorial.html
HIPAA and its regulations (the "Privacy Rule" and the "Security Rule") protect the privacy of an individual's health information and govern the way certain health care providers and benefits plans collect, maintain, use and disclose protected health information ("PHI"). Principle Investigators and study personnel are required to take the Level 5 HIPAA training. http://hipaa.stanford.edu/
SIR (Sponsor–Investigator Research) training conducted by staff from Spectrum OTC or CCTO for any Stanford PI who is conducting sponsor–investigator research and holds his or her own IND from the FDA.

(continued)

Box 4.13 (continued)

SIR training must be completed prior to initial IRB approval; RCO staff conducts regulatory document review annually prior to continuing IRB approval.

4.4.6 Need Help?

Visit Spectrum Operations, Training and Compliance at the beginning of any clinical or translational research project at Stanford: spectrum.stanford.edu. Call 650-498-6498 or e-mail clinicaltrials@med.stanford.edu at any stage in your research with questions on any subject. Or send an e-mail to studyfacilitator@stanford.edu for expert guidance, even before you get started.

Box 4.14: The Bottom Line

Become familiar with your institution's policies, regulations, and support structures for the conduct of human research. They exist to protect you, your subjects, and your institution.

Chapter 5
Commercialization and Entrepreneurship

Daria Mochly-Rosen and Kevin Grimes

As academic researchers, some of us may be interested in forming start-up companies to develop and market the drugs that are based on our research. Others may be happy to license our technology and findings to an existing company. Knowing how to evaluate potential drug markets and effectively pitch to investors will help both groups of academicians. With so much intellectual property generated in academia, a well-researched commercial assessment and an organized and effective pitch can make potential licensees or investors take notice. The goal is not to recapitulate the sophisticated marketing plans drawn up in industry, but to highlight the project's potential and show some industry savvy. This chapter provides guidance on evaluating the commercial potential of the project, pitching to potential licensees, approaching venture capitalists, and funding the development of not-for-profit programs. The chapter also discusses legal and practical considerations, should the academic decide to form a start-up company.

5.1 Selecting the Market for Your Drug

Liliane A. Brunner Halbach

D. Mochly-Rosen (✉)
Chemical and Systems Biology, Stanford University School of Medicine, 269 Campus Drive, Center for Clinical Science Research Rm 3145a, Stanford, CA 94305-5174, USA
e-mail: sparkmed@stanford.edu

K. Grimes
Chemical and Systems Biology, Stanford University School of Medicine, 269 Campus Drive, Center for Clinical Science Research Rm 3145c, Stanford, CA 94305-5174, USA
e-mail: kgrimes@stanford.edu

D. Mochly-Rosen and K. Grimes (eds.), *A Practical Guide to Drug Development in Academia*, SpringerBriefs in Pharmaceutical Science & Drug Development,
DOI 10.1007/978-3-319-02201-7_5,

Developing a drug is expensive and success is not guaranteed. Only a fraction of products entering phase 1 testing move forward to a phase 3 clinical trial and even fewer into registration. Often, there are multiple potential clinical indications for a product under development. Before conducting preclinical animal studies, it is important to revise your discovery-stage Target Product Profile (TPP) to include the attributes desired in a clinical candidate. A thorough market assessment of the opportunities and liabilities in the clinical indications you are considering will help prioritize where you have the largest probability of success and what benchmarks to set in your TPP during the development phase. For any indication, this requires (a) identifying drug characteristics that add value for patients, physicians, payers, and regulators; (b) evaluating competing treatments; and (c) highlighting the unique advantages of your therapy that will help build your share of the market.

5.1.1 Understand the Disease

Understanding the market requires first understanding the disease. How many potential patients are there? Diagnosis rates depend on various factors: the severity of the symptoms, availability of effective treatments, disease awareness among the population, and the availability of simple and definitive diagnostic tests. Consider for example attention-deficit hyperactivity disorder. Although ritalin was available starting in the 1960s, there was an explosion in prescriptions in the 1990s as the medical diagnosis of ADHD became more accepted and public knowledge of available treatments grew. Emergence of new diagnostics or screening of a potential high-risk group (e.g., survey questionnaire for autism spectrum disorders, systematic screening for hepatitis C in baby boomers) can transform disease epidemiology and alter the size of the diagnosed patient population [1, 2].

Box 5.1: Factors That Determine Market Size

- Diagnosis Rate: How many new cases are diagnosed each year?
- Treatment Rate: Of the diagnosed, how many patients seek treatment?
- Patient Adherence: Do patients take the medication as prescribed?
- Patient Subpopulations: Would subdividing the patient pool create a more homogeneous response to treatment or disease progression, etc.?

Not all patients who are diagnosed will be treated. The treatment rate depends on factors such as the efficacy and safety of available treatments, price and reimbursement conditions, the convenience of the dose schedule and formulation, and marketing. Identifying the reasons for differences between diagnosis and treatment rates will highlight areas where your development candidate can improve upon existing treatments. Another factor to consider is patient adherence. Do patients fill their prescriptions and fully follow the dosing schedule? Reasons for deviation from the prescribed course of treatment can reveal other opportunities to improve. Sometimes it is as simple as changing the packaging, for example to blister packs with the days marked for birth control pills, or altering the formulation, e.g., from an injectable to an oral dose.

Oftentimes, disease indications have subpopulations of patients, grouped by severity of symptoms, response to certain treatments, genotypic markers, or other stratifying factors. Age can be a differentiating feature as well, with geriatric and pediatric populations often requiring different doses and safety profiles than a general middle-aged population. Consider whether your new therapy will target a specific subpopulation of patients or the whole range. Targeting a subset of patients (ideally with a predictive diagnostic test) can improve response rate, reduce the size of the clinical trials needed to show efficacy, and support premium pricing for your product. On the other hand, treating subpopulations shrinks the market size and can slow patient enrollment in trials. Trastuzumab (Herceptin®) for patients with HER2 positive breast cancer is a well-known case of targeting a specific patient subpopulation. New cancer therapies are often first tested in patients who have failed first-line treatments, as the acceptable safety profile is lower for these patients. If you are developing a new cancer therapy, it is important to consider how effective your drug will be in this subpopulation.

Once you know all about the number and make up of people affected by your disease indication, you can research where the unmet needs are. Talk to key opinion leaders in the disease to get their impressions. This includes physician specialists in the field, patient advocacy groups, disease foundations, and regulatory agencies. You may even want to talk to hospital administrators or payer representatives if reimbursement strategies are potential development hurdles. Consult Box 5.2 for a list of questions to consider when meeting with these groups.

Box 5.2: Identifying Unmet Needs

There are a variety of players to consider when developing a new drug or diagnostic. Here are some areas to consider when identifying unmet needs in an indication:

Patients

- What is current standard of care (including surgical options)?
- Are patients satisfied with current treatment options?
- How is their quality of life?
- Are they fully adherent to treatment?
- Is dosing schedule or formulation inconvenient, resulting in missed doses?

Physicians, nurses and caregivers

- What challenges exist in treating this disease?
- Is the disease well managed with current treatment?

(continued)

Box 5.2 (continued)

- Are there dose-limiting interactions with other drugs?
- How is current treatment given (e.g., in hospital, at home)?
- What access to medical care do patients typically have?
- How are patients identified (e.g., referral to specialist versus primary care physician)?
- Is recruitment difficult within this patient pool (e.g., lots of competing trials)?
- Is there a way to identify patients who will respond to treatment?

Hospital administration/regulatory/payers

- What studies are required for registration with the FDA?
- How costly would a trial be in this indication (size, duration, endpoints)?
- Are there special regulatory hurdles in this patient population?
- Is reimbursement difficult?
- What is necessary to prove cost-effectiveness in clinical development?

Others

- Are there synergistic collaboration opportunities (e.g., teaming with a diagnostic to identify responsive patient subpopulations)?
- Who are the competitors, and how strong are they in this indication?

5.1.2 Evaluate the Competition

You might assume that developing a therapy for a highly prevalent chronic disease is the most attractive commercial option. A lot of factors—such as higher requirements for safety, larger clinical trials, existing competitive treatments (establishing bars for price and efficacy), low-cost generics, and competing programs reducing market share and patient enrollment in clinical trials—can make your development program very long and launching expensive in this type of indication. Understanding the competitive environment is essential for predicting the unmet needs of the future market into which your potential product will be launched.

Competition from existing therapies and other products in development will reduce your market size. Building a competitor map will help identify the needs of the future market and define realistic expectations for market share. For each indication considered, research the different targets affected by competitor molecules: listing the pros, cons and possible consequences of modifying each target. Are the targets in the same pathway? If so, what are the competitive products' efficacy, side effects, and pharmacokinetics? Is the dose-limiting toxicity a direct result of action at the intended target or an off-target effect? If your drug target is known, are other molecules under development or on the market known to modify this target? It will take on average 9–12 years to develop a new drug, so it pays to consider other products currently in development. Just as we learn from failed experiments, look for past programs that have failed to reach market launch or been recalled. These programs may highlight issues with preclinical animal models not accurately predicting human efficacy, toxicity liabilities in your molecule or pathway, or the need to divide patient subpopulations to see a benefit in clinical trials.

If there are other competitors in the indication or target, reducing the time to market for your program is essential. Try to identify and mitigate any regulatory or manufacturing hurdles in your development plan to save time and money. Efficacy and safety bars will be much higher for products that are second to market, and their pricing and market share will be lower than if they were first to market. Ease of use is an important differentiator from immediate and future competitors. Generic molecules with a similar mode of action will drive down pricing and make it harder for you to recoup the development and registration costs for your new therapy. Look up the patent expiry dates for competing molecules and include them in your competitor map; reference Sect. 4.1 for more direction.

5.1.3 Define the Opportunity

Use the market expertise gained in the research described above to define a compelling and competitive TPP. Where are the biggest opportunities to benefit patients? Focusing on these gaps when moving your development candidate forward will improve your chances of success in the drug development process. Your knowledge of the patient burden and gaps in clinical care will allow you to estimate how many people will use your drug. Understanding the competitive landscape will allow you to refine your estimate of market share and pricing. While academic drug developers are not bound by the financial bottom line of for-profit entities, having a well-researched market analysis will give you credibility as you pitch to potential partners.

In the end, your clinical candidate TPP should support a Unique Selling Proposition (USP). The USP defines the key attributes for success of your product on the market with patients, physicians, and payers. The USP is a marketing version of the TPP and will help outline the investment opportunity for people who partner with you or license your work. Successful market launch is a long way off, but thinking about the market early will help your team's chances of reaching the goal. For a more detailed description of the numbers that go into a commercial assessment, please see the next section.

5.2 Commercial Assessments

Julie Papanek

Companies, inventors, and investors complete commercial assessments to estimate the future revenue of a potential new therapy. Revenue from product sales provides funds for research and discovery investments, drives investor interest, and finances the delivery of products to patients. During the R&D stage of a product, commercial assessments inform whether the expected revenue is likely to provide an attractive financial return on the millions of dollars invested in the drug development process.

Although it is unlikely that you will have to create a highly detailed commercial assessment as a translational scientist, identifying the key drivers will enable you to understand the market and product characteristics that make companies and investors take notice.

Box 5.3: How Many Potential Markets Should You Analyze for Your Drug?

If your drug may be used for multiple indications, evaluate only two to three markets and ignore the rest. Some companies, institutions, and investigators spend lots of time evaluating each and every potential market in which a drug could be possibly be used. This is a waste of time and resources. Most pharmaceutical companies believe in gated investing, which means that the drug must show promising activity in the first few indications before more investments are made. Focus on evaluating the first two to three indications where the product could launch and then list areas for future exploration without valuations. It will save you time and give you credibility.

5.2.1 The Formula

Most pharmaceutical companies use the same formula when estimating annual sales:

$$\text{Market size (number of potential patients)} \times \text{Product share (\% taking your product)}$$
$$\times \text{Price per patient (paid for your product)} = \text{Annual sales revenues}$$

Think of the formula like a pie chart. The market size is the entire pie. The product share is the size of your product's slice expressed as a percentage. Price per share estimates the dollars that will be charged for the product and converts units into dollars instead of number of patients in a given year.

This simple formula makes it easy to see trade-offs between different commercial and development strategies. Some companies prefer to pursue very large markets where there are lots of competitors because even a small slice of a big pie will provide a large return. Markets for statins, anticoagulants, and angiotensin receptor blockers are good examples. Other companies might choose to develop products for smaller markets with high unmet medical needs, few competitors, and few pricing constraints. In these markets, a larger product share and higher price per course of treatment can offset a small patient population to ensure adequate revenue.

Companies and investors seek to maximize the commercial potential of their products. Decision-makers focus on the variables that can be manipulated or influenced and have the largest impact on value. Let us explore each of these drivers so that we can see where drug development decisions impact commercial value.

5.2.2 *Market Size*

The market size is the number of patients with a specific disease who could be treated with a product in a given year. Start with the number of patients who are diagnosed with the disease each year. This initial number can then be adjusted up or down to reflect potential patient subpopulations or changes in diagnosis rates, treatment rates, the incidence of the disease, and the product's expected FDA label statement. When estimating changes in incidence, diagnosis and treatment rates, consider external factors such as the (in)convenience, cost, and behavioral changes your product may impose upon physicians, nurses, and patients. These considerations are discussed more in the previous Sect. 5.1.

The expected FDA label statement is directly within the control of the team designing the clinical trials, in particular the pivotal trial(s), for a new product. The eligibility criteria for patients participating in the phase 3 studies will inform the FDA approved indication statement, which then drives which patients will receive the new product once it is approved. Diagnostic tests, drug–drug interactions, minimal vital sign requirements, age, race, gender, and other patient characteristics can all dramatically change the number of patients who can receive a product. Each of these constraints should be taken into account when estimating the market size.

Box 5.4: Real World Example

When estimating the market size for crizotinib, a drug approved for anaplastic lymphoma kinase (ALK) positive non-small-cell lung cancer, Pfizer needed to take into account the drug's specificity. Fewer than 2,000 of the 221,000 patients diagnosed with lung cancer each year actually harbor the ALK mutation and are expected to respond to crizotinib. When the FDA approved the drug in 2011, its use was restricted to patients with advanced stage non-small-cell lung cancers that express the ALK gene. As a result, the FDA label reflected an approved market size of 2,000 patients; not 221,000 patients.

The inclusion criteria not only impact the commercial value but also the trial size, timelines, and probability of meeting the primary endpoint. Larger markets tend to require larger numbers of enrolled patients and more expensive clinical trials. As a result, trade-offs in phase 2 and phase 3 trial design should be debated by diverse teams including clinicians, biostatisticians, and commercial representatives.

5.2.3 Product Share

The product share estimate is usually the most subjective and heavily debated aspect of a valuation. Market share predicts the percentage of patients you expect to be prescribed your product. In the end, most companies are looking for products that are first to market and/or the best drug on the market versus the competition. Better products and very novel products tend to have product shares closer to 100%. Competition includes any and all therapies or procedures that can be used to treat a disease—not just drugs with the same mechanism of action. Surgical procedures and lack of treatment should also be considered as competition. Do not just include marketed products, as products in late stage development (phase 3) and products that are similar to your product but ahead in development are all competitively relevant.

That being said, identifying each and every drug in development is not necessary. However, it is critical to know:

1. Current options:
   - Are physicians, patients, and payers satisfied with the current options available?
   - What criteria would motivate them to switch to your product?
2. Similar products:
   - How many other products are being developed in the same market with the same or similar mechanisms of action as your products?
   - When will they launch?
   - How is your product better?
3. Other novel approaches:
   - Approximately how many other products being developed in the same market have a different mechanism of action?
   - Which are most promising?
   - When will they launch?
   - How is your product better, the same, or worse?

Notice the emphasis on speed and competitive differentiation. Speed determines the time between your product's launch and when competitors launch. Is your product first to market? If not, how far behind will it launch versus the top competition? When a product is launching a year or more after a similar competitor, the second product will have a much harder time displacing the entrenched market leader. As a result, the second product will almost always have a smaller market share. Speed also influences the duration of patent coverage after market launch. Most investors want at least 5 years of patent protection after launch to allow time to recoup development costs before facing competition from generics or biosimilars.

If a product is not first to launch, it must be better than the competition in order for it to garner significant market share. Differentiation is a product's uniqueness in comparison to other options available to treat a specific disease or condition. Put yourself in the shoes of the physician or patient. What characteristics of a product matter most? If you were treating patients with a lethal disease, would the dosing schedule of a drug matter as much as its efficacy? No, a less convenient drug that saves patients lives will be more attractive. Talk with a few physicians who specialize in the indication your product would treat—they will quickly tell you which product attributes are most important to them and the majority of their patients. Patient advocacy groups are also good resources to identify characteristics that add value. Their level of excitement about your product versus alternative options will give you a strong sense for the percentage of eligible patients who would likely receive your therapy.

Finally, keep in mind payers' priorities when calculating product share. Consider whether your product is more cost-effective or improves patient outcomes over competitors. Make sure your reimbursement strategy at a high level is not a hurdle to physicians and patients adopting your product. As you move closer to launch, a detailed reimbursement strategy will be required.

Combining speed, differentiation, and competition, you will be able to make an educated guess about the product's market share. As a rule of thumb, a product will only be broadly adopted if it is better than existing options based upon criteria that matter. If a market has many undifferentiated competitors, speed matters most. Therefore it is not surprising that companies pursue most aggressively those therapies that could be first-to-market or best-in-class.

Box 5.5: Deciding on a Market Share Percentage

Weighing the importance of speed, differentiation, and number of competitors is highly subjective. There is no right answer. Similarly, precision down to the exact percentage point is not the goal. Instead, forecasters just want to ensure they are in the right range (0–15%, 15–30%, 30–60%, 60–80%, 80%+). The best evidence to support an assumption is analogies from similar products and similar markets. For instance, if a company is developing a rheumatoid arthritis therapy that will likely have lots of competitors, examples from the TNFα inhibitor market would be informative.

5.2.4 Price

The final step in the formula is converting the number patients treated with your product into sales revenues. The conversion is simply canceling units and will be dependent upon the product's dosing schedule. Here is an example conversion:

1 pill per patient per day × 7 days per week × 12 weeks of therapy × $20 per pill = $1,680 earned per patient completing a full course of therapy

While the dosing schedule and frequency will likely be fixed in the clinical design, the pricing estimate is unquestionably flexible. The same competitive assessment of speed, differentiation and competition that informs product share also informs pricing. If a product meets a significant unmet medical need and dramatically improves outcomes or standard of care, a higher price (*a.k.a.* a premium price) can be charged and will likely be reimbursed by insurance companies. On the other hand, if a product is similar to the competition, a premium cannot be defended.

Leveraging existing pricing estimates from the current standard of care is a good starting point. The pricing of imiglucerase (Cerezyme®), Genzyme's enzyme replacement therapy for Type 1 Gaucher's disease provides a great example. Before Shire started selling its competing product, VPRIV®, Genzyme could charge $200,000 per patient per year for imiglucerase. Shire undercut Genzyme's price by approximately 15% at launch in order to gain market share since its product did not offer a significant clinical advantage.

5.2.5 Making Informed Decisions Early

Before moving promising therapeutic candidates forward into preclinical studies, take the time to consider how your decisions will impact the commercial potential of your product. Decisions made in late-stage research impact the market size, potential product share, and pricing flexibility of a drug. Preclinical studies determine the design of clinical trials that, in turn, determine the commercial label approved by the FDA. Labeling determines the scope of the sales force needed and insurance reimbursement. Be particularly thoughtful when considering:

- In which disease should this product be studied first?
- Which patients should be included in the clinical trials?
- How far before/behind the competition will this product launch?
- Is this product better than alternative options as defined by patients, physicians, and payers?

Just by thinking through these four questions, you will be well on your way to estimating the value of your product as well as understanding the commercial implications of your decisions. Fortunately, investors and companies do not expect detailed valuations from you. They will emphasize whether you understand how your product will fit into the competitive landscape and how this impacts its ultimate value.

Box 5.6: The Bottom Line

Before investing in a novel therapeutic, investors (e.g., a company or venture firm) will want to ensure that future revenues will justify the development costs and provide a positive return on investment. When analyzing potential future revenues, it is important to take into account the number of eligible patients (total market), your product's market share, and price. Pricing and market share will depend upon the unique advantages that your product offers over existing therapies and other potential new competitors.

5.3 Making a Compelling Pitch to Potential Investors

Leon Chen

Effectively communicating your pitch to potential investors is a critical skill in attracting the necessary resources for starting a company. While investors may vary significantly in their criteria for evaluating new opportunities, common themes and practices can help entrepreneurs better communicate their ideas. This section reviews both substance and style of a successful pitch.

5.3.1 What Is the Problem?

There are fundamental questions that every pitch should address. First—what is the problem you are trying to solve? Second, perhaps less obvious but equally important—who cares? An understanding of which technical improvements in efficacy, safety, or convenience will result in a significant commercial opportunity can be a more challenging question to answer. A compelling pitch to investors should not only address the problem, but also demonstrate that it is a problem the market will pay to solve.

5.3.2 What Is the Solution to the Problem?

Moreover, is your solution commercially practical and viable? To realize their full potential, technically elegant solutions to difficult problems must also be convenient and fit easily within the current commercial environment. A common trap that innovators fall into is to assume that because they can solve a very difficult technical problem, physicians and payers will naturally change behavior to incorporate their novel solution. A discussion of the pros and cons of your innovation from the point of view of patients, prescribers, and payers can help clarify the likelihood of clinical and market acceptance. You must convince potential investors that your solution is both feasible and attractive to those who will drive its adoption.

5.3.3 How Do You Know That the Solution Will Work?

Since investors are not likely to be educated in the background science, describing the evidence supporting your solution is clearly important in convincing them of the value of the proposition. However, in an initial pitch, the scientific background is often overly lengthy and loses the attention of investors. As a top scientist in your field, investors will typically trust that your knowledge of the background science is sound. Be careful not to overshadow raw data with general background and not to make this section overbearing.

Box 5.7: The Basics of Every Pitch

1. What problem are you trying to solve?
2. What is your solution to the problem?
3. How do you know the solution will work?
4. Who else is trying to solve this problem?
5. How big is the opportunity?
6. What will it take to achieve success?

5.3.4 Who Else Is Trying to Solve This Problem?

This question is typically simplified into an overview of the competition. When describing others in the field, it is important to compare your solution not only to existing products, but also to those in development. An early stage company must understand both today's market and what the market may look like when its product is going to compete. Simply listing the competition is not as valuable as a description of the technical approaches and how your solution compares. Analogous to scientific presentations, investors will assume you are an expert in your field. A thorough understanding of the competitive landscape is an impressive indication of a well thought out opportunity and a demonstration of that expertise.

5.3.5 How Big Is the Opportunity?

One or two slides are typically sufficient to cover the market opportunity. If the target market segment is well understood to be large and underserved, do not spend significant time going through the market. If the target market is a niche segment that is more complicated to explain, it is valuable to help investors understand the size of the opportunity. Frequently, the larger the market size, the more time innovators want to spend discussing it when, in fact, it should be the inverse. A lack of interest in discussing the market size may not be due to lack of interest, but rather because it is not controversial. Consider carefully how much explanation the market warrants and the unique information you can present here to enlighten potential investors.

5.3.6 What Will It Take for This to Be a Success?

A successful presentation will lay out a high level vision of a business plan and path forward. For product-based companies, an overview of the necessary steps and time to commercialization should be included in your pitch. Technology based companies should focus on what would be necessary to enable a platform technology to the next meaningful step. Diagnostic companies should be capable of outlining plans into commercialization and what the requirements would be to generate revenues and get to cash-flow break even. Importantly, innovators should have a general sense of financing needs to get to the next inflection point as well as cash needs to reach overall success. The near term financing needs form the basis of the "ask" in any pitch.

5.3.7 The Style

These above points cover the basic content of any successful pitch. The next section will focus on style of presentation and how one can best prepare for a successful delivery.

Unlike the typical audience when you give an academic talk, investors vary widely in their background, reflecting a broader range of technical, medical, and business experience. When preparing for an effective pitch, it can be invaluable to learn about the investors' areas of expertise and the kind of companies in which they invest. Much of this information is publically available, so do your homework.

Understanding your audience can help you tailor your pitch—adjusting the amount of scientific background, setting speed and pace of delivery, and anticipating likely questions based upon the investors' background. The goal of a presentation is to provide a concise, yet informative overview of your business concept. The initial pitch should provide a clear view of the overall vision without getting bogged down in too many details. As a general rule, the presentation should not be overly lengthy. The key challenge is including all the relevant information in the presentation while maintaining efficiency. Knowing your audience allows one to speed up and slow down when necessary and to incorporate slides that convey the necessary information.

Box 5.8: Thoughts About Style

1. Know your audience.
2. The pitch is an engaging discussion.
3. Highlight challenges and limitations.
4. Prepare to pitch by pitching.

5.3.8 Prepare to Be Interrupted

Scientific presentations are typically structured as a complete presentation followed by questions and answers. In contrast, a successful business pitch should be an engaging conversation. One should expect and hope for a back and forth discussion covering a range of questions that can take the presentation in a variety of directions. While this can be disruptive and disconcerting when giving a presentation, successfully navigating this type of presentation is often an indicator of a well-communicated story. The ability of an innovator to engage in conversation covering a diverse set of topics beyond the science itself is a very positive sign.

5.3.9 Point Out the Limitations

No business plan is perfect. The most compelling business pitches do an excellent job of identifying and addressing the most significant challenges and limitations. In many cases, the most challenging aspect of a plan cannot be solved technically. The solution may be sought in different business strategies, regulatory tactics, and/or future research to identify new approaches. Avoiding a discussion of these hurdles delays the inevitable, whereas addressing them proactively will contribute to an engaging discussion and demonstrate a well thought out development plan.

5.3.10 Practice, Practice, Practice

With so much to cover and the uncertainty of what will stick with potential investors, what is the best way to prepare for a successful pitch? The most effective way to refine your presentation is to practice your pitch with other industry veterans. Investors or otherwise, people with varying industry backgrounds will help identify questions and challenges that are likely to arise. In these risk-free discussions, one can learn how to answer the questions effectively, as well as strategies to address potential challenges one might face.

Box 5.9: What Surprised an Academician?

When looking for funding to start KAI, we talked to hundreds of people: from industry friends, to academicians, entrepreneurs, and many, many investors. We learned a great deal from these presentations, and—as expected—heard endless numbers of 'no's. The key was to treat each new pitch as the one that would secure us the funding. Optimism, determination, and being really well prepared eventually got us what we needed.—*DM-R*

5.3.11 Drug and Diagnostic Pitches

Apart from the general commentary on what makes a successful pitch, there are some specific considerations that a therapeutic drug or diagnostic business plan should address. Clinical and regulatory strategies are critical to the success of any drug development path. Business plans focused on developing a novel therapeutic should thoroughly understand clinical signal to noise, patient selection for enrollment and the regulatory attitude towards novel drugs in the therapeutic area of interest. For example, stroke is historically an area where clinical signal to noise makes it challenging to show a clinical benefit. Oncology has become an area where many drug developers have benefited from biomarkers to aid in patient selection. Diabetes and obesity are therapeutic areas where the current FDA focus is on safety as opposed to efficacy. All drug development plans should be particularly aware of these issues with respect to their therapeutic strategy.

Box 5.10: Ask the Experts

Although academic researchers are often not familiar with many of the issues related to drug development, take the time and learn them. There is ample literature as well as information on the web. Consult practicing physicians in the field as well as regulatory scientists and clinical trial experts. Talk to as many of them as you can and learn who is also a key opinion leader (KOL); consider recruiting KOLs to your advisory board.

Diagnostic innovations face very different hurdles from drug companies. Novel diagnostic solutions often face challenges in adoption because they require physicians to change their routine of managing patient flow. Diagnostic innovators should be aware of their target physicians, the typical patient flow and how the new test can be best integrated into current practice. Another challenge many diagnostic companies commonly face is getting payers to reimburse for a novel test. Diagnostic innovators should be well aware of the process of applying for the necessary reimbursement codes to realize the commercial potential of their test.

Box 5.11: Common Challenges

1. Common drug development challenges include clinical signal to noise, patient selection, and regulatory strategy.
2. Common challenges for diagnostic companies include changing physician behavior to adopt a novel test and obtaining reimbursement from payers.

5.3.12 Summary

A compelling pitch to potential investors covers a broad set of topics while communicating the message in a concise manner. This section touched briefly on many of the topics that should be included in your pitch. Entrepreneurs should be prepared for an engaging discussion with investors that can lead in a variety of directions. The best way to prepare for a presentation is to pitch to industry experts with a diverse set of backgrounds. With each interaction, one can gradually refine and improve the presentation to better suit the next investor audience while also preparing the entrepreneur for any direction the pitch may take.

5.4 Venture Capital Funding

Kevin Kinsella

More than any other industry, biotechnology has been the handmaiden of venture capital. The original companies (Cetus and Genentech) were financed by venture capitalists. A veritable finance ecosystem grew up around biotechnology—consisting of early, mid and late stage venture capital, pharmaceutical companies, specialized investment banks, skilled analysts, mezzanine investors and the investing public. They were all eager to share in the upside of this novel late twentieth century industry that promised revolutionary new diagnostics and therapeutics for clinical medicine.

Forty years after the founding of Cetus, the biotech industry has indeed delivered on its promise of creating novel diagnostics and therapeutics, many from completely novel technologies: recombinant DNA, monoclonal antibodies, genomics, combinatorial chemistry, ultrahigh throughput screening, etc. Yet, in spite of these technical *tours de force*, as an investment class, biotechnology has been a net consumer of cash—more aggregate money has been invested in these novel products than they have ever garnered in aggregate revenues.

Box 5.12: What Surprised an Academician?

Despite great scientific and clinical promise, the biotechnology industry overall has lost money since its inception. As a result, exit options and return on investment can be limited for venture-backed biotechnology companies that are still in development.

This sobering realization dawned in the aftermath of the small cap stock market bust in 2000 and led to the erosion of the financial support pillars for the biotechnology industry. After more than a decade, the initial public offering (IPO) market has not recovered, although there have been increasing numbers of biotech IPOs in recent months. The biotech-specialized investment banks have disappeared along with their analysts who followed the industry. This leaves acquisition by pharmaceutical partners as the likely exit strategy for most biotech start-up companies. This lack of competition has made it much more difficult for the venture investors to extract value when their companies are acquired by pharmaceutical companies.

Box 5.13: Key Terms and Abbreviations

IP: intellectual property
IPO: initial public offering of stock
NDA: new drug application to the FDA
NPV: net present value
EVA: economic value added; an estimate of total profit minus the cost of financing the capital
Pre-money value: a company's value before a particular funding event. This determines how much of the company is owned by the previous investors.

What does all this mean for biotech entrepreneurs seeking venture capital for their novel ideas? There are still venture funds that do invest in biotech but the ambit of their reach has diminished. In the Golden Age of biotech investing (1980–2000), one could start a company around an idea, a mere target, a *Science* or *Nature* paper, and have a go at success. Today, since history has shown that no one can depend on the "kindness of strangers," *viz.*, the buyers of stock or pharma partners—the venture syndicate backing a biotech enterprise must comfortably have all the cash already around the table that the company might need to take a product to market. Since, notwithstanding the size of some biotech venture funds ($500–$1 billion), it is hard to form a syndicate greater than $60–80 million tranched over several years, virtually all opportunities need to fit into this Procrustean bed. If they do not, they probably cannot get financed.

There is a "template" that Avalon Ventures uses—at a high level—to look at opportunities and it may be useful for the biotech scientist/entrepreneur to get on the same page with venture capitalists on their opportunities:

5.4.1 Opportunity Assessment: A Template

- Is there a market which is both attractive enough financially while also being *accessible*?
- Does the team have access to world-class people who can provide input to the project or process?
- Will the activity happen in our lifetime? Projects often follow the 4/2 rule; they take four times as long and cost twice as much money as anticipated or the reverse: they cost four times as much and take twice as long.
- Is the IP robust and do we really understand the technology and have the skills internally to make it happen? If not, can we easily outsource those skills? Who are the current or potential competitors in this technology space?
- Do we have the finance for the end game? It is often easy to find funds to start an initiative, but not that easy to obtain the necessary funds for completion. For example, the development process needs to be fully thought through in terms of, say, pre-money values based upon achievement of specific milestones.
- Finally, there is the alpha factor. One needs a high tolerance for bad news. When a particular initiative is undertaken, unanticipated hurdles will inevitably occur; so one needs to have the persistence and determination to meet the goals for the end game. In short, you need to love the game you have chosen to be in. If not, do not do it.

Not many projects get caught on the filter or sieve when assessed by the above criteria, but for those that do, the final selection process depends upon a robust financial analysis. In short, you need to love the project but it also has to pay the rent. There are many ways to skin this cat (NPV, break-even analysis, EVA, Monte Carlo techniques, etc.), but they generally all point in the same direction. For example, a negative NPV or never reaching a break-even point is not a good sign.

5.4.2 Strategy to Succeed

So what do we at Avalon Ventures expect from an academic entrepreneur who is pitching their program? We want entrepreneurs to be students of the industry. In some cases, the technology for new investment will rely heavily on the breakthroughs of the past investment era (recombinant DNA, monoclonal antibodies, genomics, combinatorial chemistry, ultrahigh throughput screening, etc.). How are entrepreneurs improving upon these technologies to get drugs into and out of the clinic more efficiently? Avalon has always invested in technology, including all of the inventions mentioned above from the last era. We are now interested in clever applications of these disciplines (which were once just inventions) to improve the risk/reward ratio.

And it is really all about risk/reward. Since our downside is losing our entire investment, the upside has to be pretty spectacular. Therefore, we look for dramatic, breakthrough science that can be in the clinic within 2 years. This means that the work has to have progressed quite far from just target discovery. There has to be a molecule (protein or small molecule), which has some compelling animal data, and has no red-flag toxicology concerns. The IP must be strong and there needs to be significant competitive intelligence—which usually means that the academic lab must be on top of its game and generally recognized to be the thought-leader in the field. We need to be able to license or option the IP on reasonable commercial terms and to enter into exclusive (as to the technology in question) consulting arrangements with the company's academic founders. For us, no management team needs to be in place (but this is *not* typical of venture funds). We prefer to invest tranches of capital as milestones are met. Start with $500,000–1,000,000. Follow that with $2–3 million and perhaps a total investment of $7–10 million over several years.

Box 5.14: What Surprised an Academician?

When searching for funds, remember that venture capitalists can bring a great deal more to the table than their firm's financial support. For example, KAI's initial investor, Skyline Ventures, provided critical mentorship to the founding team, offered rent-free working space in their offices, helped assemble a cross-functional team of consultants for our virtual company, and played a leading role in securing additional investors for the series A financing. While money is indispensable when starting a company, also consider the additional support that a firm offers when selecting your VCs.—*DM-R*

We are looking for a round-trip of our capital (cash needs to come back as cash) in a 4–7 year time frame. Venture firms are typically 10 year limited partnerships and hence capital—as cash or a liquid (public) security—needs to be returned to the limited partners (the investors of the VC fund) during the fund's lifetime.

Despite an upswing in IPOs in recent months, it is risky to count on an IPO as an exit strategy. As a result, we build companies for acquisition. As such, partnerships with pharma companies on products are a very dicey proposition. In the Good Old Days, pharma partnerships "proved" to the investment community that you were a company worthy of public investment. Since the IPO market is limited, partnerships often are just "bear-hugs" from pharma that permit them to outsource R&D (financed largely by venture capital since the deals are usually skinny and back-ended), where the biotech company ends up being attractive to only one or few suitors. Hence, there is a trend to autarchy in biotech venture funding, where venture syndicates form toward fully financing a company through a phase 3 clinical trial or NDA.

Box 5.15: The Bottom Line

If the IP is breakthrough, the team A-class, the opportunity massive, the funding modest and the timeline is years, not decades, successful exits can still be had in biotech. And venture capitalists are always looking for these opportunities.

5.5 Not-For-Profit Drug Development

Eugenio L. de Hostos

Statements about "not-for-profit drug development" (NPDD) are often followed by questions like, "Is there such a thing?" and "Does that even work?" The short answer to both questions is yes.

NPDD for neglected tropical diseases (NTDs) is becoming more common due to a convergence of scientific, business, and social trends. Globalization has led to a raised awareness of the medical needs of the poor in the developing world and at the same time brought to bear new philanthropic, industrial and governmental resources on those needs. However, the resources available for NTD drug development still pale in comparison to the concentrated and vertically integrated resources available to a conventional pharmaceutical company working on drugs for profitable indications. For this reason, the key to NPDD is the ability to harness scattered financial, material, and technical support from a variety of sources for a given project [3].

Box 5.16: Key Terms and Abbreviations

NPDD: Not-for-profit drug development
NTD: Neglected tropical disease
PDP: Product Development Partnerships
AMC: Advanced Market Commitments
OOPD: Office of Orphan Products Development
FDA: US Food and Drug Administration
PRV: FDA's Priority Review Voucher
NDA: New Drug Application with the FDA
NME: New Molecular Entity; a new drug submitted to the FDA Center for Drug Evaluation and Research (CDER)
NIAID: National Institute for Allergy and Infectious Diseases
TRND: Therapeutics for Rare and Neglected Diseases

In the past decade, a new breed of not-for-profit organizations called Product Development Partnerships (PDPs) has emerged. PDPs such as PATH, DNDi, and OneWorld Health (OWH) have brought the rigor and expeditiousness characteristic of large pharmaceutical companies to the arena of NTD vaccine and drug development. The impact of PDPs is impressive and one study suggested that some 75% of NTD drug development is now conducted by organizations of this kind [4].

With the advent of high-throughput screening facilities in academic institutions and an increased interest in NTDs among students and professors alike, academia has become a breeding ground for early-stage drug-development projects. Not only are more targets being validated, assays developed, and compounds discovered, but also academics are increasingly involved in advancing these discoveries into drug products. But many academic projects still stall due to lack of expertise and resources when it comes to pharmaceutical development. PDPs can play a critical role in turning academic projects into drug development programs and shepherding development candidates through the preclinical "valley of death" [5, 6].

As discussed earlier, screening hits and motivation alone are insufficient to bring a new drug to market. PDPs can be clever about picking and executing projects and can maintain lean operations, but there is no fundamental reason to expect NPDD to be cheaper than conventional drug development. Just like any biotech or pharmaceutical company, PDPs can keep their costs down through outsourcing drug development services. Organizations like OWH and DNDi have gone as far as becoming completely lab-less and thus "virtual"—focusing on project building and management while relying exclusively on the services of contract research organizations around the world for lab work and manufacturing.

Repurposing of drugs is another cost-saving option for PDPs. OWH, for example, repurposed paromomycin, an off-patent antibiotic approved for human use decades earlier, for the treatment of visceral leishmaniasis by conducting the requisite phase 3 studies. Similarly, the veterinary pharmacopeia, particularly in the field of antihelminthics, is a good place to look for drugs with "crossover" potential; these can be developed for human use more quickly and at a lower cost than when starting from scratch [7]. It is important to keep in mind, however, that repurposing still requires, at the very least, phase 3 studies, which are usually the most expensive part of drug development. Another important consideration regarding repurposed drugs is that, in the end, the new product may fall far short of the ideal target product profile. For this reason, the financial advantage of repurposing has to be weighed against the long-term utility of the product.

On the income side, of course, things are very different and more challenging for NPDD than for conventional drug development. As long as not-for-profit drug development remains not-for-profit, philanthropy will remain the "secret sauce" that makes NPDD possible. It is basic capitalism: social goods that will not generate sufficient profit to motivate the commercial sector require funding by government and philanthropic agencies instead.

Box 5.17: What Surprised an Academician?

Academics can advance their drug development projects for diseases of the developing world by partnering with a philanthropically funded Product Development Partnership or government program, such as the NIH's TRND.

Grants from organizations such as the Bill and Melinda Gates Foundation,[1] the Wellcome Trust and the World Health Organization's Special Programme for Research and Training in Tropical Diseases (TDR) are the lifeblood of many PDPs, but in-kind donations from the pharmaceutical industry are also very important. For example, a number of pharmaceutical companies have provided generous support to OWH's Diarrheal Diseases Program, including technical advice, access to compound libraries, drug discovery and preclinical services. That being said, the mantra of PDPs is to become less dependent on philanthropy and to find a way of becoming more sustainable. Financial sustainability not only allows long-term strategic planning, but also provides greater flexibility in incubating early-stage projects and exploring new development possibilities.

One possible strategy that can help sustain a PDP is to include in its development portfolio a drug product that has dual markets—that is, a profitable, rich-world market and a not-profitable, developing world market. For example, a drug to treat cholera that could also be sold to treat traveler's diarrhea could help support other projects in a PDP's pipeline. In the area of vaccines, Advanced Market Commitments (AMCs) are being used to incentivize the development and production of new products. An AMC is simply a promise by a sponsor to purchase a certain amount of vaccine product at a certain price once development is complete. This mechanism has been used to incentivize vaccine manufacturers to make flu vaccines and is now being used to promote NTD vaccine development.

Another small but wealthy market that can potentially support the development of NTD drugs is the military. For example, the US Department of Defense[2,3] supports drug development in areas of military and national security importance, which in some cases overlap with NTDs. PDPs can also benefit from a range of government resources and incentives such as those offered by the National Institutes of Health (NIH) and the Food and Drug Administration (FDA). These resources are spread out and each alone is unlikely to support a single development phase in its entirety, let alone a complete drug development program. However, resources are available and an NPDD program can be greatly aided by access to them, though timelines are likely be extended. The NIAID's Division of Microbiology and Infectious Diseases[4] also offers drug development services ranging from discovery to phase 1 trials through government contractors. The NIH also offers a program called Therapeutics for Rare and Neglected Diseases (TRND)[5] that makes available the expertise and resources of institutes such as NIAID, in effect establishing an ad hoc PDP with the applicant. TRND, for example, serves as a portal for resources at NIAID earmarked for work on schistosomiasis and hookworm disease. Services offered through the TRND umbrella are also available to applicants from outside the USA.

On the regulatory side, the FDA[6] has developed several programs intended to encourage development of treatments for diseases neglected by the pharmaceutical industry. The Orphan Drug Act was enacted to reduce the costs of developing drugs for diseases that affect less than 200,000 patients per year in the USA or drugs not expected to recoup their unaided development costs, both categories that include NTDs. The Office of Orphan Products Development (OOPD) has the responsibility of facilitating orphan drug development by finding regulatory shortcuts that can save time and money. One of the mechanisms that the OOPD promotes is the repurposing of existing drugs from the human and veterinary pharmacopeia.

Another program that has generated great expectations is the FDA's Priority Review Voucher (PRV) program mandated by the US Congress in 2007 to promote drug development for less profitable indications. Under the program, any organization that obtains approval of a New Drug Application (NDA) for a new molecular entity (NME) to treat a disease on their list of NTDs is granted a transferable PRV.[7] The potential value of the voucher lies in the fact that it gives the bearer the right to an expedited review of another NDA application for a drug that need not be for the treatment of an NTD. Obviously this could incentivize a big pharmaceutical company to take a second look at shelved projects that may have potential for the treatment of an NTD. However, what excites the PDP community the most is that PRVs can be sold to a third party, such as a pharmaceutical company seeking to shorten the time-to-market of its new blockbuster.

PDPs are hoping that their NTD drug projects will generate PRVs for which large pharmaceutical companies may be willing to pay millions of dollars, allowing them to build endowments and invest in other NPDD projects. The PRV mechanism could potentially also attract private capital into NTD drug development projects that would otherwise provide no financial return on investment. Unfortunately, the value of PRVs, in financial terms as well as practical terms of actual regulatory time saved, has been widely discussed but remains very speculative. Pharmaceutical companies and philanthropic organizations are waiting for the day when a market for PRVs develops and a stimulus is felt in the NTD field.

5.5.1 Conclusion

Bringing new drugs to market is a complex and expensive process, but not-for-profit drug development is possible, is happening, and is arguably more feasible than ever before. In this resource-constrained corner of the pharmaceutical world, Product Development Partnerships will continue to take a leading role in effectively harnessing a wide range of scattered public, industrial, academic, and philanthropic resources to fill in gaps in the treatment of neglected diseases.

Box 5.18: Web Site Resources

[1]www.gatesfoundation.org/vaccines/Pages/advanced-market-commitments-vaccines.aspx
[2]www.dtra.mil/Missions/ChemicalBiologicalDefense/ChemicalBiologicalDefenseHome.aspx
[3]www.jpeocbd.osd.mil/packs/Default2.aspx
[4]www.niaid.nih.gov/labsandresources/resources/dmid/pages/default.aspx
[5]www.trnd.nih.gov
[6]www.fda.gov/forindustry/developingproductsforrarediseasesconditions/default.htm
[7]www.bvgh.org/What-We-Do/Incentives/Priority-Review-Vouchers.aspx

5.6 Legal Aspects of a Start-Up Biotechnology Company

Alan C. Mendelson, Peter E. Boyd, and Christopher M. Reilly

The first question that entrepreneurs must ask when they are thinking about starting a biotechnology company is whether it is the right time to form a business entity. Should the entrepreneurs formalize their relationship around a commercial opportunity or continue to grow their research and development activity within the comfort of a university?

The decision should be driven by a cost–benefit analysis: Do the benefits of forming a business entity now outweigh the initial and ongoing costs of maintaining it? There are certain benefits that apply across all industry sectors. For example, most business entities, if properly structured and capitalized, provide limited liability—shielding officers, directors, and investors from personal liability for the liabilities incurred by the business.

Box 5.19: Key Terms and Abbreviations

IP: intellectual property
Bayh–Dole Act: US legislation regulating intellectual property generated by government-funded research
LLC: Limited Liability Companies
S-Corps: Subchapter S corporations
C-Corps: Subchapter C corporations
Angel investor: a wealthy individual or group who provide capital for start-ups
VC: venture capital
Vesting: the legal process of granting stocks or options whose full value accrues over time

However, for biotechnology entrepreneurs, especially those coming out of a university setting, there may be additional, unique considerations in deciding whether or when to form a business entity. University researchers have access to lab space, administrative personnel, core service centers, library facilities and related infrastructure that are an expensive component of running a start-up. Academic investigators are eligible for research grants and can conduct investigator-initiated clinical studies at a fraction of the cost of an industry-sponsored study. Furthermore, staying within a university setting may also provide a more reliable source of income for the entrepreneurs.

On the other hand, remaining in a university setting generates additional risks above and beyond the generic costs associated with forming an entity (e.g., registration fees, attorneys' fees and the costs associated with maintaining a company). For example, the university will retain ownership of any intellectual property (IP) developed by its employees. Therefore, entrepreneurs must balance the benefits of licensing their technology early and owning any future IP that is developed against the benefits of developing the technology within the university and licensing more IP at a later stage. Any IP licensed from the university will be subject to royalty payments and the Bayh-Dole Act of 1980, which, among other things, requires the licensee to try to manufacture the invention in the USA. Most life science companies with a presence in the USA are familiar with the Bayh-Dole requirements, but it can complicate negotiations with some international acquirers down the road, especially companies in Japan.

In sum, if the entrepreneurs are still investigating whether there is a commercial opportunity and can leverage the advantages a university has to offer, it may ***not*** make sense to form a business entity. However, once the entrepreneurs have determined that there is a viable business opportunity and want to begin building a company, raising funds or hiring employees, forming a business entity may be critical to moving the opportunity forward.

Box 5.20: What Surprised an Academician?

When forming a start-up company, academic founders should engage an experienced corporate attorney very early in the process before signing any transaction. The attorney will protect the interests of the founders throughout the process and provide helpful information regarding such issues as negotiating licensing agreements, how much ownership they should expect to retain after VC funding, hiring and other essential processes. Further, it is prudent to retain your own lawyer to represent your personal best interests, rather than to rely on the university, VC, or company lawyers.—*DM-R*

Once entrepreneurs determine that it is time to form a business, they must select the best type of entity for their business. Business entities fall into two broad categories: those that are subject to "pass through" taxation and those that are not. In pass through entities, the profits and losses of the company are passed through the company to the investors and only taxed once. Pass through entities include partnerships, Limited Liability Companies (LLCs) and Subchapter S Corporations (S-Corps). The more common Subchapter C Corporation (C-Corp) is a non-pass through entity where income or losses to the corporation and dividends distributed to shareholders are taxed separately. When selecting the appropriate entity, entrepreneurs should assess all the options based on what will work effectively, without creating too much of a burden on a limited administrative staff, and whether the platform chosen is flexible enough to meet both the short-term and long-term goals and challenges of a growing biotechnology company.

Biotechnology companies are capital intensive and take an extended period of time to generate predictable revenues, so entrepreneurs need to ensure that all possible funding sources remain open. Two common funding sources at the outset are angel investors and venture capital firms (VCs). VCs will ***not*** invest in pass through entities because they create negative tax consequences for their limited partners, many of which are tax-exempt institutions. If the entity is going to approach VCs, it will need to be structured as a C-Corp. Occasionally, a few wealthy individuals are prepared to fund the early research and want pass through taxation so that they can write off their investment currently. It is extremely unlikely, however, that these angel investors will be able to fund the company beyond its early research phase, so, at some point, the entity must be converted to a C-Corp to raise capital from institutional investors.

Partnerships and LLCs require relatively complex governing agreements that tend to be time consuming and expensive to create and explain to investors and early employees. These additional costs associated with forming and operating an LLC or partnership combined with pass through taxation make them inappropriate for almost every biotechnology start-up. Whereas it is possible to form an S-Corp for pass through taxation and convert it to a C-Corp when the company is looking to raise venture capital, most investors recognize and will insist that the long-term benefits of the rights, preferences and privileges of preferred stock permitted under Subchapter C outweigh the short-term benefit of pass through taxation. In our experience, almost every biotechnology company decides to incorporate as a C-Corp once they have considered the flexibility and benefits that a C-Corp can provide.

Assuming that the entrepreneurs select a C-Corp as their desired entity, they will next need to select a state of incorporation. Most institutional investors are used to investing in Delaware corporations. Delaware also has a well-developed body of corporate law and is efficient in dealing with corporate issues at both the administrative and judicial levels. In addition, dealing with the California Secretary of State's office remains cumbersome and can significantly delay the completion of a financing round. However, choosing to incorporate in Delaware will require the company to qualify to do business in its state of operation and to incur a second, relatively small franchise tax. On balance, most biotechnology companies are formed as Delaware C-Corps.

Recruiting and maintaining the best team is a key component of success for every biotechnology start-up. Therefore, entrepreneurs will want to ensure that they can effectively attract and compensate talent. At the outset, the entrepreneurs will want to determine who is going to be a founder. The concept of who is or who is not a founder can assume a significance not warranted by any legal recognition or long-term consequence. However, being identified as a founder often provides the entrepreneurs with a certain psychic benefit. In addition, the founders typically assume a greater level of risk than employees, consultants, or advisors who join the company after funding has been obtained. Thus, the founders are normally granted the opportunity to purchase equity at a nominal cost when the corporation is initially formed, simply because there is little value present at that time other than the basic concept or idea.

Whether stock is sold just to the founders or to a broader group of employees, consultants and advisors, it is important to document the initial allocation of equity to mitigate the risk of future disputes among the contributors to the enterprise and to ensure that all stock and option issuances are made in compliance with the securities laws. In this regard, the entrepreneurs must come to grips with the fundamental decision of whether to require vesting of the stock or options to be issued—for themselves and future employees, consultants and advisors—and what type of employment or consulting agreement should govern the various individuals' service relationships. Under a vesting scheme, founders and employees are allowed to purchase a block of common stock, but only gradually gain full ownership of that stock on the time frame described in the vesting schedule. Vesting is quite common and is more protective of the entrepreneurs *vis-à-vis* each other and of investors, but stock subject to vesting will likely require a filing under Section 83 of the Internal Revenue Code and more time and expense with counsel.

In any event, making sure that every contributor is party to some form of proprietary invention and assignment agreement granting intellectual property rights to the company should be a requirement of all parties to the enterprise. In evaluating these issues, entrepreneurs need to be mindful that potential investors are unlikely to invest if they do not have comfort that key personnel are committed for the long-term and that the company's IP is being protected.

After the above core issues have been addressed, entrepreneurs need to consider the size and structure of the company's board of directors, as well as any special governance provisions that ought to be included in the company's charter or bylaws. An experienced emerging company corporate lawyer can guide the entrepreneurs through all of these issues and help the company document key decisions, develop a set of standard documents to be signed by employees and consultants, obtain a tax ID (an Employer Identification Number) so that the company may open a bank account and pay employees, and make all state and federal regulatory filings associated with the sale of securities in a timely manner.

Box 5.21: The Bottom Line

Biotechnology start-ups face a unique set of challenges in growing from a few founders performing research to a fully funded development company with product candidates to explore. Like the start of any significant business, it is essential that entrepreneurs take the proper first steps as they pursue an opportunity from idea to business entity and beyond.

Box 5.22: Resources

1. Aronson DH (2011) Venture capital: a practical guidebook for business owners, managers and advisors, 5th edn. Available at http://noromoseley.com/documents/VCGuidebook5thEd-FullwAnnexes.pdf
2. Bagley CE, Dauchy CE (2008) The entrepreneur's guide to business law, 3rd edn. The Thomson Corp., Mason, OH
3. Kolchinsky P (2004) The entrepreneur's guide to a biotech startup, 4th edn. Available at http://www.evelexa.com/resources/startup_guide.cfm
4. Top Ten Legal Mistakes Made by Entrepreneurs, Harvard Business School Working Knowledge (Mar 3, 2003) http://hbswk.hbs.edu/item/3348.html
5. US Small Business Administration, Incorporating Your Business, http://www.sba.gov/category/navigation-structure/starting-managing-business/starting-business/establishing-business/incorporating-registering-you-0

5.7 Founder Preferred Stock

Scott M. Iyama and Stephen J. Venuto

The convergence of unpredictable access to capital and extended corporate life cycles in the current life science market can lead to misdirected incentives and significant personal risk on the part of founders. The use of Founder Preferred Stock aims to mitigate the risk to these founders and operates to align the incentives to maximize the long-term value of the company. This is a brief summary of the potential advantages and uses of Founder Preferred Stock.[1*]

[1] The contents of this publication are for informational purposes only. Neither this publication nor the lawyers who authored it are rendering legal or other professional advice or opinions on specific facts or matters. The authors and Orrick assume no liability in connection with the use of this publication.

IRS Circular 230 disclosure: To ensure compliance with requirements imposed by the IRS, we inform you that any tax advice contained in this communication, unless expressly stated otherwise, was not intended or written to be used, and cannot be used, for the purpose of (1) avoiding tax-related penalties under the Internal Revenue Code or (2) promoting, marketing or recommending to another party any tax-related matter(s) addressed herein.

5.7.1 *What Is Founder Preferred Stock?*

Founder Preferred Stock is nearly identical to Common stock, except for a very important conversion right: Founder Preferred Stock can be converted into shares of the stock sold by the company in an equity financing. For example, an entrepreneur holding shares of Founder Preferred Stock may elect to convert some or all of the shares of Founder Preferred Stock into shares of Series A Preferred Stock, Series B Preferred Stock, etc., at the time of a financing. This unique feature of Founder Preferred Stock facilitates a transaction where an entrepreneur can sell an interested investor the same series of Preferred Stock issued by the company in an equity financing, on the same economic terms.

By way of example, in a Series A Preferred Stock financing where the company is selling Series A Preferred Stock at $1.50 per share, an entrepreneur holding 100,000 shares of Founder Preferred Stock and 900,000 shares of Common stock can sell an interested investor 50,000 shares of Founder Preferred Stock for $75,000. The investor purchasing such stock will acquire 50,000 shares of Series A Preferred Stock (as a result of the conversion) and receive the same rights as if the investor purchased the shares directly from the company. The entrepreneur will walk away with $75,000, receive the benefit of the value created by the company at the time of the financing, and still hold 95% of his or her equity in the company.

5.7.2 *Objective of Founder Preferred Stock*

As illustrated by the example above, the objective of Founder Preferred Stock is to provide an entrepreneur a limited, but meaningful, amount of liquidity in exchange for the sale of a small proportion of the entrepreneur's equity at an early stage of the company's life cycle. The liquidity is not intended to provide a windfall to the entrepreneur, but rather, the proceeds from the sale of Founder Preferred Stock are aimed to lessen the stress and risks to an entrepreneur while concurrently providing a potential reward for reaching a key milestone.

Core to the functionality of the Founder Preferred Stock are two key features that operate to align the incentives of the entrepreneurs and the investors. First, the sale of Founder Preferred Stock removes the need of the entrepreneur to manage toward a premature exit in order to remove undue personal risk associated with founding and self-funding the company. Second, since the capitalization is structured so that the Founder Preferred Stock represents only a small portion of the total equity held by an entrepreneur (typically 10% or so), the entrepreneur is incented to maximize the value of his or her equity stake and recoup as much upside as possible. The cumulative effect of these features is that the entrepreneur is better situated for the long life cycle of a life science company and is aligned with the investor to maximize the value of the company over the full term of such a life cycle.

5.7.3 Advantages of Founder Preferred Stock

5.7.3.1 Common Stock Pricing

A key attribute of Founder Preferred Stock is that the sale of Founder Preferred Stock does not, by itself, have a material impact on the valuation of the company's Common stock. In the standard form of founder liquidity, the entrepreneur sells shares of Common stock held in the company (which sale affects the valuation of the common stock for future grants). This sale creates an inherent tension between the interest of the entrepreneur, who wants the highest price, and the company that wants to keep the price as low as possible (to continue granting lower priced securities to its employees). With the use of Founder Preferred Stock, the entrepreneur gets the benefit of the negotiated valuation with the investor and the company gets to keep the Common stock price as low as possible to incentivize employees and new hires.

5.7.3.2 Predictable Capitalization

The implementation of a Founder Preferred Stock structure creates a blueprint for early liquidity. Rather than trying to negotiate opportunities for liquidity with both the entrepreneurs and investors, the use of Founders Preferred Stock provides a readily available mechanism that can be used without further complication. In addition, the investors purchasing the shares of Founder Preferred Stock do not need to negotiate any special rights as they are receiving the identical security that the company is issuing in the equity financing.

5.7.3.3 Potential Tax Advantages for Entrepreneurs

If the stock is held for more than 1 year, a key advantage to the use of Founder Preferred Stock is that an entrepreneur can argue that the proceeds from the sale are subject to long-term capital gains tax. Alternative structures such as common stock sales, stock repurchases and cash bonus programs can result in ordinary income tax treatment for any proceeds received by the entrepreneur (which are typically much higher than long-term capital gains tax).

5.7.3.4 Long-Term Incentives for Entrepreneurs

By providing early liquidity and reducing the personal risk to the entrepreneur, the company incents the entrepreneur to build value for the duration of the company. Frequently, this mitigation of personal risk is a more powerful motivational tool than vesting schedules, equity allocations and other typical forms of founder incentives.

Box 5.23: The Bottom Line

A Founder Preferred Stock structure can realign incentives and reduce the personal risk of an entrepreneur, all while providing material advantages to the company. The implementation of Founder Preferred Stock, however, requires a careful consideration of the company's business objectives, as well as key tax and legal issues. All of such considerations should be explored as early as possible in the formation process of the company by the business and legal partners.

5.8 Plan, Organize, Motivate and Control

John Walker

With your lead program, capital and investors in hand, you might be tempted to believe that your work is done. After all, you have come a long way since your initial discovery in the lab or clinic. But the realization soon hits that you now have to execute on that pitch that you have made to the venture investors. This section is about how to lay the foundation for building a successful company.

In simple terms, this requires understanding some basic principles of running a business; namely the need to **plan** what you intend to do, **organize** your people and resources to accomplish the plan, **motivate** your team to accomplish tasks in a timely manner, and finally, implement a **control** mechanism to keep your company on course.

Box 5.24: Key Terms and Abbreviations

SWOT: Strengths, Weaknesses, Opportunities and Threats; analysis used to assess the company/project and plan accordingly.
MBO: management by objective
Org chart: organization chart; indicates functions in the organization and the reporting structure
360° evaluation: evaluation of an employee (or future employee) by supervisors, peers and those who report to that individual.
All hands meetings: a periodic company meeting that provides an update to all the employees. This is a powerful and simple tool to motivate and control.
Board of Directors: the group of individuals representing investors/owners who set the strategic direction and have ultimate decision-making authority for the company.

5.8.1 Plan Your Course

The planning process can be broken down into several key elements. The first is a clear and understandable **mission statement**, a short paragraph or sentence that reflects the long-term vision of your new company. For example: *To develop and commercialize new treatments for solid tumors based on the modulation of kinases*. When developing a mission statement, consider the company you intend to have 10 years from now, not that which you have today or will have next year. The mission needs to be aspirational, and each word should be carefully selected to convey the vision clearly and concisely.

Closely following the mission statement, articulate a **value statement** for your company. The value statement will guide the development of the company culture that will best help you accomplish your goals. For example: *We will conduct our research in a rigorous, peer-reviewed process; we will achieve our business objectives in an open and transparent manner; we will recognize the value of each of our associates and encourage diversity in thought and experience*. The main point is to think about the type of company you want to be and state that as clearly as possible.

Box 5.25: What Surprised an Academician?

I initially felt that this "kumbaya" exercise was somewhat embarrassing and that the company's mission, culture, and long-term goals should be obvious. Through working on these with the team, I realized that they were not clear even to me.—*DM-R*

Now that you know the long-term vision of the company, as well as the type of company that you want to create, the next step is to outline just how you intend to get there. This requires a multi-year **strategic plan**, one that should look ahead at least five years. Because the biotechnology and biopharma industries, like many others, are volatile and changing rapidly, this strategic 5-year plan should be reviewed and revised on an annual basis. In developing a strategic plan, it is critical to be open and honest about your capabilities (strengths) and areas for improvement (weaknesses). One approach is called an environmental analysis, also referred to as a SWOT (Strengths, Weaknesses, Opportunities and Threats) analysis (Fig. 5.1).

A comprehensive and honest assessment of your strengths and weaknesses will help determine which elements of your business need to be preserved, strengthened or changed. Ideally, this exercise will allow you to focus on the most critical issues for success, including intellectual properties, capital, investor base, management team, scientific capabilities, board of directors, employees, skills, scientific advisory board, etc. Make it clear that this analysis is for internal use. Importantly, in

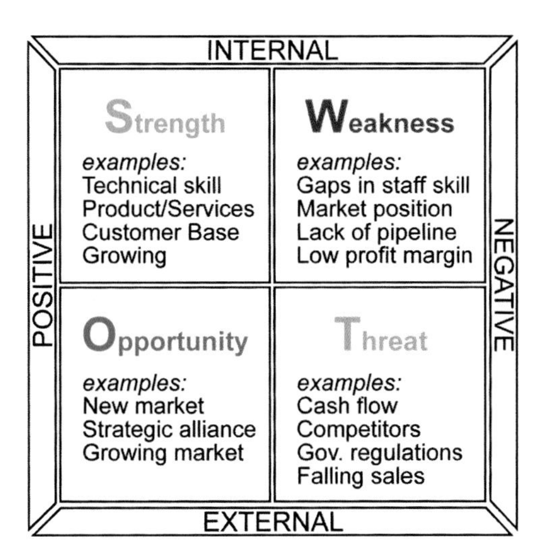

Fig. 5.1 SWOT analysis chart

going through this exercise, recognize that there are no "sacred cows"; everything about the company should be analyzed and debated as either a strength or a development need.

Once you have reviewed your strengths and weaknesses, assess the opportunities and threats your company faces. This requires an examination of trends in the market, conditions for raising new capital, prospects for company partnerships, competitors, the FDA, changes in clinical practice and changes in the health insurance or payer landscape. Review all of the external issues that may have a bearing on your company's success.

Consider the following statement of a threat: *The FDA is increasingly concerned with safety, narrowing the severity and types of adverse events allowed in treating cancers.* Obviously this observation will have an effect on your ability to reach your eventual goal of commercializing new treatments for solid tumors, since FDA approval is necessary for introducing a product to the market. Explicitly identifying this as a threat provides an early guidepost for planning your clinical development activities.

With a mission, values statement and environmental analysis in hand, now you are ready to start reviewing the goals and strategies that will help you achieve your desired outcome. This part of the planning process should incorporate five to eight overall goals that can be accomplished within the 5-year horizon of the plan, and the strategies that will need to be employed to reach each one. An example would look as follows:

Goal:

By the end of the planning horizon, we will have completed a phase 2b study on our lead program demonstrating an increase in survival of more than 6 months in pancreatic cancer.

Strategies:

1. Advance two lead compounds to toxicity studies by the end of the first 6 months of operation.
2. Nominate one of these compounds for clinical development by year end.
3. Complete a phase 1/2 study in 25 subjects at four centers by the end of the second full year of operation.
4. Complete enrollment of 75 patients at eight different centers in the US and Europe as part of the phase 2b study by the end of year 3.

In developing your goals, remember to touch on all of the key aspects of your company. These should include product and clinical development, capital formation strategies, personnel policies and philosophies, business development goals, etc.

You will find that a good strategic plan will flow naturally into an annual operating plan (budget) for the next year, allow you to set individual MBO (Management by Objective) goals for all of your key people, align the work of the team, provide measurable milestones for determining your progress and allow you to more successfully articulate your company's vision and goals to outside parties such as prospective investors, partners, and employees.

Box 5.26: What Surprised an Academician?

We all know about teamwork; after all our labs are teams of scientists. However, in a company, we truly have a single goal—the success of the company. The difference is apparent from the day of your first board meeting. It is exhilarating.—*DM-R*

5.8.2 Organize Your Resources

With the plan now in hand, you can set about getting your company organization in place. This does not just refer to an **organization** (Org) **chart**, but rather the systems you will need to put in place to realize your goals. The members of your Board of Directors, Scientific Advisory Board, Clinical Advisory Board, executive team, and scientific staff must possess the requisite expertise to accomplish your plan. As an example, if one of your goals is to raise a new round of financing in year 2, then hiring a Chief Financial Officer may be an important strategy to articulate within the first year of operation; if partnerships are important, than a Business Development function may be critical. The timing and need for a Clinical Advisory Board will also be more apparent once the plan is in place. Use the plan as your guide in developing your organization at all levels, recognizing the fluid nature of the skill sets and expertise that you will need at different time points in your plan.

5.8.3 Motivate Your Team

Highly motivated personnel are critical to accomplishing the company goals in the desired time frame. Appropriate incentives can help maintain the desired corporate culture and ensure that individual and collective interests are aligned. It is important to recognize that most people are not motivated by money, which is more of a "hygiene factor," but rather by such things as the scientific merit of the project they are working on, their relationships with coworkers, and the belief that the company values them both as individuals and for the contributions they make to the organization.

Box 5.27: What Surprised an Academician?

Sometimes academics make the incorrect assumption that, because companies are engaged in for-profit drug development, industry professionals are chiefly motivated by money. In fact, many in industry are motivated by being part of the process to alleviate human suffering. Many are idealists!—*DM-R*

While many of these factors may seem intangible, they are critically linked to your company's culture, management practices, and personnel policies. These should be specifically addressed in your planning process. For example, if you state that you want to have a performance-based culture, then are you putting in place those types of incentives that reward and recognize success? Do you have hiring practices that allow for interviews that determine "cultural fit" to the organization? Does your practice call for interviews on a 360° basis (i.e., do potential direct reports have the chance to interview their prospective new boss)? Do you have a promotion-from-within philosophy, where individuals can advance their careers as opportunities present themselves within your organization? Do you want to establish a bonus program at selected levels or all levels in your company? Is the bonus based on clearly stated and quantifiable goals? Do you practice open and honest communication to all of your associates? An easy way to accomplish this is to hold monthly "all hands meetings," where many, or all aspects of the company are presented and discussed with all employees. The combination of promising scientific programs with an open, honest culture that values individuals will lead to employee retention, satisfaction, and team building.

5.8.4 Control Your Progress

Once you are up and running, the last item to consider is that of control. Perhaps this is more easily understood as "knowing if you are still on track." The first step to ensuring that you keep on track is to monitor and measure achievement in real time.

A common mechanism for tracking progress is to compare budgeted expenses versus actual expenses. Perhaps equally important, management should monitor progress against stated objectives and timelines on a routine basis. Further, if you have a bonus program for all employees, then reporting progress on a regular basis (perhaps at those monthly all hands meetings) is important. If important goals are not being accomplished in a timely fashion, it is critical to determine the cause, refocus your efforts, and take corrective actions to ensure the on time delivery of your objectives.

Box 5.28: What Surprised an Academician?

When KAI decided to terminate one of the clinical programs, I attended the failure party—despite my doubts on the appropriateness of celebrating such an event. The management emphasized the excellent work conducted by the team to "fail fast." By showing lack of a path forward, the team freed a clinical group and budget to focus on another indication earlier. The failure party was also an opportunity to recognize the team's hard work on failure analysis, which could help the company succeed the next time.—*DM-R*

Box 5.29: The Bottom Line

Plan what it is you intend to do.
Organize your people and resources to accomplish the plan.
Provide *motivation* for accomplishing the plan.
Provide *control* mechanisms to keep you on course.

References

1. http://www.cdc.gov/Features/CountingAutism/
2. CDC press release recommending hepatitis C testing for US baby boomers. http://www.cdc.gov/nchhstp/newsroom/2012/HCV-Testing-Recs-PressRelease.html
3. Nwaka S, Ramirez B, Brun R, Maes L, Douglas F, Ridley R (2009) Advancing drug innovation for neglected diseases-criteria for lead progression. PLoS Negl Trop Dis 3(8):e440
4. Moran M (2005) A breakthrough in R&D for neglected diseases: new ways to get the drugs we need. PLoS Med 2(9):e302
5. Emmert-Buck MR (2011) An NIH intramural percubator as a model of academic-industry partnerships: from the beginning of life through the valley of death. J Transl Med 9:54
6. Moos WH, Kodukula K (2011) Nonprofit pharma: solutions to what ails the industry. Curr Med Chem 18(22):3437–3440
7. Olliaro P, Seiler J, Kuesel A, Horton J, Clark JN, Don R, Keiser J (2011) Potential drug development candidates for human soil-transmitted helminthiases. PLoS Negl Trop Dis 5(6): e1138

Chapter 6
Concluding Thoughts

Daria Mochly-Rosen and Kevin Grimes

During the twentieth century, advances in drug therapy came fast and furious, resulting in the cure of many previously fatal diseases such as pneumonia, tuberculosis, and testicular cancer. Treatments for more chronic diseases (e.g., asthma, heart failure, hypertension, and diabetes mellitus) have improved the duration and quality of life for untold numbers of patients. These new therapies arose from basic research discoveries followed by the application of the scientific disciplines of drug discovery and development. In recent years, the cost and time required to bring a new drug to market has escalated dramatically, resulting in the contraction of the biopharmaceutical sector—particularly in the basic research component of the industry. This raises the question of where our next generation of drugs will originate. Academicians are well positioned to fill this gap in the discovery pipeline. Free from the pressures of generating a short-term financial return on investment, we can focus on drug development projects that address the greatest unmet clinical need. Once projects are appropriately "de-risked," they can be licensed to existing biopharmaceutical or start-up companies for further development. If we agree that academia has a social responsibility to ensure that new drugs reach patients in need, we must be willing to devote more financial and human resources to this applied science endeavor. We will need to develop the facilities and expert staff/faculty in such disciplines as assay development; high-throughput screening; medicinal chemistry; pharmacokinetics and ADME; toxicology; and regulatory science. We believe that if we in academia fail to take on this expanded role, we

D. Mochly-Rosen (✉)
Chemical and Systems Biology, Stanford University School of Medicine, 269 Campus Drive, Center for Clinical Science Research Rm 3145a, Stanford, CA 94305-5174, USA
e-mail: sparkmed@stanford.edu

K. Grimes
Chemical and Systems Biology, Stanford University School of Medicine, 269 Campus Drive, Center for Clinical Science Research Rm 3145c, Stanford, CA 94305-5174, USA
e-mail: kgrimes@stanford.edu

D. Mochly-Rosen and K. Grimes (eds.), *A Practical Guide to Drug Development in Academia*, SpringerBriefs in Pharmaceutical Science & Drug Development,
DOI 10.1007/978-3-319-02201-7_6,

may be depriving future generations of novel therapies that will save lives, improve health, and lower the escalating costs of health care.

6.1 A Call to Action: Changing How We Pursue Drug Discovery and Development

Steve Schow

The pursuit of wellness and ideal health has been a fundamental aspect of human existence for thousands of years. The evolution of medicines can be traced to the use of opium in the Neolithic age to alleviate that most noxious of human symptoms, pain. One can observe the increasing exploitation of medicinal agents by the appearance of ever expanding and improving pharmacopeias, from the famous Ebers Papyrus, dating from 1550 BC, and the wealth of Chinese, Indian (e.g., Caraka Samhita, Susruta Samhita), and other traditional medicine writings, to the first edition of the British Pharmacopoeia of 1864, to the modern listings of drugs in the 2013 Physicians Desk Reference.

The late 1940s through the late 1960s saw an explosion of new drugs to treat heretofore untreatable medical conditions. New and effective medicines for major psychiatric maladies, cancer, pain and inflammation, type-2 diabetes, hypertension, all kinds of infectious conditions, and even birth control came into existence during that time, thanks, in large part, to the research and development efforts of the pharmaceutical industry. Perhaps the most impressive accomplishment of that era was the emptying of the TB sanatoriums as new drugs vanquished the White Plague in the developed world. This was a time when academic and hospital-based researchers were focused on discovering potential drugs. They worked closely with the pharmaceutical industry to make those new treatments readily available to their patients and did so without gain. Between 1940 and 1966, the golden years of drug discovery, 505 (of 823 worldwide) new molecular entities (NMEs) were introduced in the USA, of which 437 (87%) originated in the pharmaceutical industry [1, 2].

The thalidomide debacle, and its subsequent removal from the market in 1962, created a public call for increased regulatory demands and oversight. This had a significant impact on drug development, increasing timelines and drug discovery costs. An industry shift of focus from patients' needs to sales and marketing, the rise of the blockbuster drug sales model and the ever shorter time horizons and demands for boundlessly increasing returns on capital by investors, led to a much maligned, unsustainable industry by the beginning of the twenty-first century.

Box 6.1: Key Terms and Abbreviations

TB: tuberculosis
NME: New Molecular Entity; a new drug submitted to the FDA Center for Drug Evaluation and Research (CDER)
PhRMA: Pharmaceutical Research and Manufacturers of America
VC: venture capital
R&D: research and development
PK/ADME: pharmacokinetics (absorption, distribution, metabolism, and excretion)
IND: Investigational New Drug application; document filed with the FDA prior to initiating research on human subjects using any drug that has not been previously approved for the proposed clinical indication, dosing regimen, or patient population
NGO: nongovernmental organization

6.1.1 Drivers for Changing the Drug Invention Landscape

By 2010, the estimated cost for inventing and registering a new chemical entity was calculated to be $1.778 billion dollars, which includes the costs for drugs that fail in the development process and the time averaged cost of capital [3, 4]. Overall, 77% of research projects are abandoned, and those costs must eventually be recaptured in drug pricing. Since 1950, the number of approved new drugs per billion dollars spent has fallen 80-fold in inflation-adjusted terms. Drivers of these skyrocketing costs are multifactorial and include: the extended time required to prove a drug is both effective and safe, the expansion of costly development activities as a result of increased regulatory demands, along with technology/scientific advancements and the risks associated with tackling poorly understood diseases. Also, the efficacy of previously approved drugs for the treatment of many medical conditions is quite acceptable—or at least good enough to seriously complicate the introduction of new treatments. The chance of failure, and therefore the cost of clinical development, is markedly increased when a new drug must show a statistical improvement over an active comparator.

As a result, the average time from discovery to approval in 1960 was 2 years, whereas it takes 14.8 years today, with the biggest jump in time coming between the 1960s and the 1980s [1, 3, 4]. Likewise, between 1993 and 2006 the size of clinical trials exploded. By 2006, the average number of patients required for pivotal oral anti-diabetic drug trials rose from ~900 to ~4,000 [5]. Merck's current pivotal trial for its novel anti-cholesterol drug, anacetrapib, will be 30,000 patients [5]. The rule-of-thumb in 1955 was 1 compound in 1,000 synthesized would become a drug [2]. Today the attrition funnel is more extreme: 10,000 compounds synthesized; 2,000 begin preclinical development; 200 enter phase 1 clinical trials; 40 enter phase 2 trials; 12 enter phase 3 trials; eight are approved and only one makes a satisfactory return on investment before the patent expires and generics enter the market [3, 4]. Seven out of ten drugs launched between 2003 and 2008 failed to cover their development costs [3, 4].

In addition to productivity issues, competitive pressure resulting from shorter patent life on new drugs, rapid market entry of competitive products and price erosion caused by generic substitution meant that the high costs identified above must be recouped over a very short period of time. For example, in 1960, a $3.5 billion industry produced 50 NMEs, with an average patent life, the time remaining for protected market exclusivity, of 16 years. By 1980, a $22 billion industry produced 12 NMEs with an average patent life of 8 years [1]. Time from launch of first in class drug to the launch of the first me-too drug has collapsed from 10.2 years on average in the 1970s to 1.2 years in the 1990s. This has a significant impact: prescriptions for Merck & Co.'s asthma and allergy treatment, Singulair®, plunged nearly 90% within 4 weeks of the introduction of competing generic copies [6]. This industry is so dependent on blockbuster drugs, like Lipitor®, that the loss of revenues because of the patent cliff for these drugs approached $200 billion per annum in the past decade. Such a catastrophic loss of revenue has devastated R&D budgets [7].

There has been substantial industry consolidation, in part driven by the trends described above: out of the original 42 PhRMA members in 1988, only 11 (25%) remained in 2011. Gone with the acquired companies is a vast infrastructure of large drug research and development campuses. There has also been a relentless reduction in scientific personnel engaged in new drug invention. In-house biotechnology discovery research efforts, including the discovery laboratories, have progressively been abandoned. The current situation is captured in the words of GlaxoSmithKline's CEO, Andrew Witty: "We've got no interest in physical facilities. We've been reducing our own. The last thing we need is a big pile of bricks with air conditioning" [8]. Initially, this evolving problem was masked by the rise in the biotech industry, but by 2000 that industry sector began to focus increasingly on late-stage clinical development activities. The recession of 2008 resulted in over 40% of venture capital (VC) firms decreasing their investment in biotech in 2011 because of low returns, stifling the founding of discovery-stage start-up companies [9].

6.1.2 Unaffordable Drugs

From the patient's perspective, this has been a disaster. Of the 39 NMEs approved by the FDA in 2012, including yet another drug for erectile dysfunction, 12 are priced in the $100,000 per year/course of treatment range [10]. At the rate of increase of new drug prices over the past 20 years, drug prices will approach $1 million per year/course of treatment 20 years hence; clearly an unsustainable cost to patients and society. From 1975 to 1999, only 10 of 1,393 new drugs marketed were for tropical diseases: 5 were from veterinary R&D, 2 were from military R&D, and

2 were reformulations of old drugs; only 1 of the 10 is truly affordable for the developing world population [11–14]. In contrast, 390 of 1,393 NMEs were for cardiovascular indications [11–14]. Despite a pressing need for new antibiotics, the industry is avoiding research in this indication because it takes 250–500 patients treated to see the same return on drug R&D investments as one person treated with a drug for a chronic condition.

We are faced with unaffordable hundred thousand dollar treatments (some of which display minor benefits for desperate patients), pricing pressure from payers, patent cliffs on blockbuster drugs, increased regulatory demands, and decreased R&D budgets resulting in marginal innovation. As a result, serious unmet medical needs are going unaddressed while the industry is preoccupied with quarterly statements. The deconstruction of the drug invention enterprise is not what patients and society need from this industry. *It is time to reconsider the role of academic, philanthropic, and government institutions in drug research and development.*

6.1.3 A Path Forward

Prior to the 1970s, academic scientists played a larger role in the discovery of new drugs. It is time to do that again; early-stage drug research and development should move back into the academic milieu and away from traditional pharmaceutical companies. The most obvious reason to return to academic-based drug discovery is the vast expanse of innovative biomedical research that occurs in institutions around the world. Academicians, as discoverers of this new science, are best positioned to appreciate the application of their science and become the champions for driving their discoveries toward the clinic to benefit patients. Academic scientists are free to collaborate with experts in other fields unencumbered by the veil of secrecy that typifies an industrial research laboratory. Additionally, the development of drugs and diagnostics can take place at a measured pace, being enriched as the new science materializes, rather than under some artificial quarterly deadline demanded by the marketplace. Products for rare, neglected, and intractable medical conditions can be pursued without the overhanging considerations of future profitability or time to market. This new approach allows for far greater risk-taking to discover truly novel medicines while minimizing the profit-driven need to create ever more expensive me-too entities and formulations of dubious value to patients and society.

6.1.4 Recreate the Discipline

Many universities are acquiring drug screening tools for identifying hit compounds against novel biological targets discovered within the walls of the university. High-throughput screening capabilities, molecular design tools, novel *in vivo* models, and *in vivo* imagining technology are now readily available in the university setting. But several nontraditional drug R&D skills need to be brought into the university environment if the goal of clinical drug candidate discovery is to be realized. These include medicinal chemistry, formulation, drug safety, and pharmacology screening.

Project management is a critical new skill that must also be added to the academic milieu in order to facilitate the advancement of projects from basic biology to clinical development candidate. Project management is required to map out the development plan, coordinate and facilitate team activities among departments within a university and across universities, ensure various participating groups fulfill commitments on time and on budget, manage intellectual property, meet regulatory requirements, and verify that supporting documentation is created and filed with authorities. Embedded within this project management function could be a small staff of part-time consultants who are experts in drug process development and pilot scale manufacturing, quality control, formulation, toxicology/safety, PK/ADME, and regulatory science. These experts can guide projects through the pre-IND stage of development. This group should also include clinicians, pharmacovigilance experts, clinical trialists, and statisticians (all available in academia already).

The new system would ultimately pass the new medical products on to venture-backed start-ups and pharmaceutical companies in need of late-stage drugs to fill pipelines. Alternatively, non-economically viable late-stage products could be passed from universities to governments or philanthropic/nongovernmental organizations (NGOs) serving the neglected and orphan patient populations for subsequent phase 3 clinical studies and registration. Governments and NGOs who subsequently complete development are positioned to distribute these medicines at little or no charge to patients or their physicians.

Since the cost of capital is about half the investment cost of a new drug, the savings should be substantial if new drug research and early-stage development is funded by society within universities and hospitals, rather than paid for by pharmaceutical companies. In addition, society would shoulder most of the costs associated with candidate failures through phase 2, which it also currently does with basic biomedical research. Therefore, drug pricing would reflect only the costs of the late-stage phase 3 trial, the CMC and registration costs, and the failure rate and capital costs for phase 3 candidates.

The average out-of-pocket costs to test an NME at phase 3 and register a new drug is $279 million [3, 4]. Assuming the industry average success rate of 64% for these two steps; this is only 16% of the current estimated cost for one NME [3, 4]. This proposed approach to new drug invention and development makes it unnecessary for industry to set lofty prices based upon the costly 15 year multi-failure process that currently defines new drug invention. Since new drugs will arise from societal funding, priority for new drugs will be much more focused on societal and patient needs rather than on market demands.

In the future, new drug discovery initiatives will come from compelling biomedical science, medical need and the insights and creativity of academic scientists pursuing the translation of frontier biomedical science into novel products for patients. Profit considerations and marketing will take a much diminished role in the creation and delivery of new medicines if society is willing to fund applied medicine at levels similar to its funding of basic science for the past 70 years. This is happening in increasing numbers of universities throughout the USA and around the world. Stanford's SPARK program is one such endeavor. SPARK funding of therapeutic and diagnostic projects allows for translation of innovative biomedical and clinical science into prototype products or identification of new clinical applications for established products. SPARK funds a greater diversity of projects than those seen in a typical industrial research setting. All of these programs target a compelling medical need, yet they might not make the cut in a commercial assessment. Much of the science is too early-stage or high risk to find a champion in a company without the "de-risking" preclinical work funded by SPARK. It is through this type of academic initiative that unexpected, truly innovative medicines will arise. Such initiatives will only expand in the future as increasing levels of drug discovery migrate from industry to the not-for-profit sector.

Box 6.2: My Vision of Drug Development Utopia

Certain academic hubs specializing in disease pharmacology models, ADME, formulation, toxicology/safety, regulatory and scale-up/pre-commercial production could be established to provide basic services to support the development of new therapeutics and diagnostics from early-stage prototypes spinning out from university and hospital laboratories around the world. Applied biomedical science departments would evolve to support drug and diagnostic development through proof-of-principle clinical studies, i.e., phase 2 clinical trials, before handing the vetted technology off to industry or government partners for late-stage clinical trials, registration, and commercialization.

As new drugs arise in an academic environment, patents should play less of a role in product pricing protection. Ideally, market exclusivity would be based upon market size and societal needs, not short-lived patents. For example, products for neglected or rare diseases could receive one to two decades of market exclusivity for significant pricing consideration, whereas drugs for vast markets in diabetes and heart disease would garner less market exclusivity. Unattractive properties for private capital could be developed by governments and NGOs and distributed at an affordable price for patients. Global agreement on this approach should make new drugs available for our most neglected diseases, as well as significantly grow the global academic drug discovery enterprise.—*SS*

Box 6.3: Resources

- Bartfai T, Lees GV (2013) The future of drug discovery: who decides which diseases to treat? Elsevier, Academic Press, San Diego
- Hill RG, Rang HP (eds) (2013) Drug discovery and development: technology in transition, 2nd edn. Churchill Livingstone Elsevier Limited
- Nighil WL (ed) (2009) Research and development in the pharmaceutical industry. Nova Science Publishers
- Pisano GP (2006) Science business: the promise, the reality, and the future of biotech. Harvard Business School Press, Boston
- Raviña E (2011) The evolution of drug discovery: from traditional medicines to modern drugs. Wiley-VCH Verlag GmbH & Co. KGaA, Weinheim, Germany
- Sneader W (2005) Drug discovery: a history. Wiley, Chichester, England

References

1. Committee on Technology and International Economic and Trade Issues of the Office of the Foreign Secretary, Commission on Engineering and Technical Systems, National Research Council (1983) The competitive status of the US pharmaceutical industry: the influences of technology in determining international industrial competitive advantage. National Academies Press, Washington, DC
2. deStevens G (1976) The interface between Drug Research, Marketing, Management and Social, Political and Regulatory Forces. In: Jucker E (ed) Progress in drug research, vol 20. Birkhauser Verlag, p181
3. Paul SM, Mytelka DS, Dunwiddie CT, Persinger CC, Munos BH, Lindborg SR, Schacht AL (2010) How to improve R&D productivity: the pharmaceutical industry's grand challenge. Nat Rev Drug Discov 9:203–214
4. Mervis J (2005) Productivity counts—but the definition is key. Science 309:726
5. Scannell JW, Blanckley A, Boldon H, Warrington B (2012) Diagnosing the decline in pharmaceutical R&D efficiency. Nat Rev Drug Discov 11:191–200
6. The Wall Street Journal report on Merck earnings, 1 May 2013
7. Alazraki M (2011) DailyFinance. http://www.dailyfinance.com/2011/02/27/top-selling-drugs-are-about-to-lose-patent-protection-ready. 27 Feb 2011
8. Financial Times piece (2011) Drugs: supply running low. http://www.ft.com/intl/cms/s/0/46d4a950-348e-11e0-9ebc-00144feabdc0.html#axzz1DaenttrX. 9 Feb 2011
9. Carrol J, FierceBiotech (2012) New biotech deals scrape record low as VC groups lose steam. http://www.fiercebiotech.com/story/new-biotech-deals-scrape-record-low-vc-groups-lose-steam/2012-07-19#ixzz2ZjTUTVcj. 19 July 2012
10. Jarvis LM (2013) New drug approvals hit 16-year high in 2012. Chem Eng News 91(5):15–17
11. Chong CR (2012) Repurposing drugs for tropical diseases: case studies and open-source screening initiatives. In: Barratt MJ, Frail DE (eds) Drug repositioning: bringing new life to shelved assets and existing drugs. Wiley, Hoboken, NJ
12. Elliott RL (2011) Third world diseases. Springer, Heidelberg, Germany
13. Muller-Langer F (2009) Creating R&D for incentives for medicines for neglected diseases. Gabler, Wiesbaden, Germany
14. Trouiller P, Olliaro P, Torreele E, Orbinski J, Laing R, Ford N (2002) Drug development for neglected diseases: a deficient market and a public-health policy failure. Lancet 359:2188–2194

Appendix: Author Biographies

Steven R. Alexander, M.D., is Medical Director, Spectrum Operations, Training and Compliance, Stanford Center for Clinical & Translational Education & Research. He is Professor and Chief of Pediatric Nephrology at Stanford University School of Medicine. He earned his M.D. from Baylor College of Medicine.

Mark Backer, Ph.D., received a B.S. in Chemistry from Stanford University and a Ph.D. in Chemical Engineering from the University of Washington. He has worked to develop biopharmaceuticals since joining Genentech as its seventh employee in 1978 and has participated in the development of seven commercial products. He is currently General Manager of Alava Biopharm Partners, a consulting group focused on CMC support for product developers. He also supports the SPARK program in an advisory role.

Rebecca Begley, Ph.D., is an Associate Manager for Regulatory Project Management at Gilead Sciences. Prior to that, she worked at KAI Pharmaceuticals as a Scientist and Project Manager. She received her undergraduate degree from Barnard College and her Ph.D. from Stanford University in 2004.

Terrence Blaschke, M.D., is Senior Program Officer, Global Health Discovery and Translational Sciences at the Bill and Melinda Gates Foundation and an emeritus Professor of Medicine in the Division of Clinical Pharmacology at Stanford University School of Medicine. His research interests include clinical pharmacology of drugs used in HIV-infected patients with a particular interest in access and quality of these drugs in less-developed countries.

Peter Boyd, Esq., worked as an associate until 2012 in the Silicon Valley office of Latham & Watkins LLP, where he represented start-up companies and venture capitalists. He has also served on the management team of a privately held medical device company. Mr. Boyd earned his B.S. in Biology from UNC-Chapel Hill and a joint J.D.–M.B.A. degree from the University of Virginia.

D. Mochly-Rosen and K. Grimes (eds.), *A Practical Guide to Drug Development in Academia*, SpringerBriefs in Pharmaceutical Science & Drug Development,
DOI 10.1007/978-3-319-02201-7, © The Editors 2014

Jennifer Swanton Brown, R.N., is Manager, Regulatory Services and Education in Operations, Training and Compliance; Spectrum, Stanford Center for Clinical & Translational Education & Research.

Liliane Brunner Halbach, Ph.D., is a consultant in the Bay Area and is currently working as a contractor for Genentech. After starting her career in the pharmaceutical industry 17 years ago in the Metabolic Disease Department at Novartis, she continued as a global Market Analyst for Rheumatology at Roche CH. A transfer to Roche Spain gave her the opportunity to work in Business Development, Marketing and Finance. Liliane has a Ph.D. in Pharmacology from the University of Basel, Switzerland.

Leon Chen, Ph.D., M.B.A., is a Venture Partner at OrbiMed Advisors, working with the private equity team on venture capital investments. Prior to joining OrbiMed, Leon was a Partner at Skyline Ventures. He was a cofounder of KAI Pharmaceuticals, a company he started with Dr. Daria Mochly-Rosen based on his work as a Ph.D. student in her lab. As a biotech entrepreneur, he has experience in drug discovery, building a research organization and has taken drugs from the laboratory into clinical development. Leon has a Ph.D. in Molecular Pharmacology from Stanford University School of Medicine, and an M.B.A. from the Stanford Graduate School of Business.

Eugenio L. de Hostos, Ph.D., M.B.A., works for OneWorld Health, an affiliate of PATH that develops medicines for the neglected diseases of the developing world. In his role as Director of Research and Preclinical Development, Dr. de Hostos manages discovery and preclinical stage projects and is involved in expanding the OneWorld Health portfolio through partnerships with other companies, academic researchers, and donor institutions. Dr. de Hostos received his B.S. in Biology from Yale University in 1983 and his Ph.D. in Biology from Stanford University in 1989. In 2010 he completed his M.B.A. in environmentally sustainable and socially responsible business from the Presidio School of Management.

Emily Egeler, Ph.D., is the Program Coordinator for the SPARK Translational Research Program at Stanford University School of Medicine, where she helps manage SPARK projects and coordinates outreach with other academic institutions setting up SPARK programs and various other internal and external projects. She received her Ph.D. in Chemical and Systems Biology from Stanford University School of Medicine.

Daniel Erlanson received his Ph.D. in Chemistry at Harvard University and completed postdoctoral research at Genentech before joining Sunesis Pharmaceuticals at its inception, where he eventually became Associate Director of Medicinal Chemistry. Dan subsequently cofounded Carmot Therapeutics, Inc., a company that applies proprietary technology to the discovery of small-molecule drugs for unmet medical needs.

Nicholas Gaich has more than 35 years of experience in areas such as supply chain management, service line economics, and clinical research infrastructure and operations. He retired in 2012 as Assistant Dean, Clinical and Translational Research

Operations of the Stanford Center for Clinical and Translational Education and Research and now runs an executive management consulting firm, Nick Gaich and Associates, and serves as a Senior Advisor to the angel investment firm Venture-Med. He received his B.B.A. with an emphasis in Healthcare Administration from National University of San Diego.

Harry Greenberg, M.D., is the Joseph D. Grant Professor of Medicine and Microbiology and Immunology and the Senior Associate Dean for Research at Stanford University School of Medicine. He has been an active NIH funded investigator for over 30 years during which time his studies have focused primarily on viruses that infect the GI tract, liver, or respiratory tree. Dr. Greenberg was the Chief Scientific Officer at a biotechnology company called Aviron (now MedImmune Vaccines), where he played an important role in bringing the live attenuated influenza vaccine to licensure.

Kevin Grimes, M.D., M.B.A., received his M.D. from Brown University and his M.B.A. from Stanford University. After his training, he joined the Stanford faculty as an academic internist. He later worked in the medical device and biotechnology sectors before returning to academia. He is currently the Co-Director of the SPARK Translational Research Program and Associate Professor of Chemical and Systems Biology at Stanford University School of Medicine, where he also teaches drug discovery and development and the practice of internal medicine.

Scott Iyama, Esq., focuses his practice on the representation of early stage technology companies, with a particular focus on life science companies and university spinouts. He is a member of the Emerging Companies Group at Orrick, Herrington & Sutcliffe LLP (Orrick). Prior to attending Stanford Law School, Mr. Iyama performed extensive biological-based research as a graduate student at the University of California San Diego and as a research assistant at Genentech, Inc. and the NASA Ames Research Center.

Carol Karp is Senior VP of Regulatory Affairs at Esperion Therapeutics. With over 30 years of experience, Carol has held leadership positions in pharmaceutical and biotechnology companies, maintaining a primary focus on innovative regulatory strategies for the development and commercialization of therapeutics and diagnostics in disease areas including cardiology, metabolic disorders, immunology, Alzheimer's Disease, analgesia, and anesthesia.

Kevin Kinsella is a graduate of MIT and the Johns Hopkins School of Advanced International Studies. He founded Avalon in 1983 and has specialized in the formation, financing, and/or development of more than 60 early-stage companies. He currently serves on the Boards of Directors of several Avalon portfolio companies. He is also the largest individual producer of the Tony Award-winning hit Broadway musical, Jersey Boys. He is a member of the Council on Foreign Relations and a member of the Broadway League.

Bruce Koch received his Ph.D. in Cell and Developmental Biology from Harvard University and completed his post-doctoral studies at the University of California at Berkeley. He joined the discovery research group at Syntex rising to the position of

Director of Discovery Technologies at Roche Pharmaceuticals. He is currently the Senior Director, Discovery and Technological Service Centers at the Stanford University School of Medicine.

Katharine Ku is the director of the Stanford University Office of Technology Licensing and is a registered Patent Agent. She got her B.S. in Chemical Engineering from Cornell University and a Master's in Chemical Engineering from Washington University in St. Louis and has worked at a number of industry and academic institutions.

Robert Lum, Ph.D., is a veteran in drug development with experience in both large and small pharmaceutical companies. In the past, he has served as the Executive Director, Process Development and Manufacturing at Geron Corporation; Vice President, Technology and Preclinical Development at Telik, Inc.; Assistant Director of Medicinal Chemistry at CV Therapeutics; and Senior Scientist at Arris Pharmaceutical. He received his B.S. in Chemistry from the University of California, Berkeley and his Ph.D. from Massachusetts Institute of Technology.

Ted McCluskey, M.D., Ph.D., has over 15 years experience in biotech, pharmaceutical and diagnostic development designing, implementing, and analyzing clinical trials. He has worked in multiple disease areas and participated in four product approvals. Past positions include Chief Medical Officer and VP Clinical at AVIIR, Inc, Senior Director of Clinical Research at SCIOS, and Medical Director at Genentech. He is a board-certified cardiologist (Interventional and Molecular) and received his M.D. and Ph.D. from Washington University in St. Louis. Dr. McCluskey is also active in Sand Hill Angels, serving as its President and on the Board of Directors.

Alan Mendelson, Esq., has been a partner at Latham & Watkins LLP's Silicon Valley office since 2000 and is the cochair of the firm's Emerging Companies Practice and Life Sciences Industry Groups. He currently serves as a member of the University of California Board of Regents and the Boards of Trustees of the UC Berkeley Foundation and The Scripps Research Institute, as well as the corporate secretary for many public and private companies. Since 1993, Mr. Mendelson has been listed in editions of The Best Lawyers in America and IPO Vital Signs. He received his A.B. from the University of California, Berkeley, and his J.D. from Harvard University.

Daria Mochly-Rosen, Ph.D., is the George D. Smith Professor of Translational Medicine, the Senior Associate Dean for Research, and a Professor in the Department of Chemical and Systems Biology at Stanford University School of Medicine and the Co-Director of SPARK. She received her Ph.D. from the Weizmann Institute of Science in Israel, and was a postdoctoral fellow in the department of biochemistry at the University of California, Berkeley. She joined Stanford University School of Medicine in 1993 and served as the chair of her department for 4 years. In 2003, her lab's basic research led to the founding of KAI Pharmaceuticals, where she served as the CSO for 1 year, and as the chair of the Scientific Advisory Committee and a member of the Board of Directors after her return to academia. She also founded ALDEA Pharmaceuticals in 2011. In addition, Dr. Mochly-Rosen served on a variety of review groups including the Peer Review Advisory Committee of the NIH and on the Council of Councils of the NIH.

Judy Mohr received her Ph.D. in Chemical Engineering from the University of Texas at Austin and her J.D. from Santa Clara University. She has extensive experience working in patent law with an emphasis in pharmaceuticals. Judy is a partner at McDermott Will & Emery LLP (Silicon Valley Office). She also supports the SPARK program in an advisory role.

Julie Papanek, M.B.A., is a Market Planning Manager with a number of years experience working in industry. After graduating from Yale University with a B.S. in Molecular Biophysics and Biochemistry, she received an M. Phil. in BioScience Enterprise from Cambridge University and an M.B.A. from Stanford Business School. Her experience in licensing and market assessment spans academic and industry institutions, including 5 years in various positions in Genentech.

Christopher M. Reilly, Esq., was a summer associate during 2011 in the Silicon Valley office of Latham & Watkins LLP. He graduated in 2012 from the University of Virginia School of Law and joined Latham's Silicon Valley office in the fall of 2012.

Werner Rubas, Ph.D., is the founder, President, and CEO of PK/ADME Consulting, LLC. Currently, he holds a Director position at NEKTAR and is responsible for preclinical PK. He has over 25 years of experience working in the pharmaceutical field in academia, start-up, mid-size, and Fortune 500 companies. In 1999 he was the co-recipient of the PHOENIX Pharmazie-Wissenscaftspreis. Dr. Rubas received his Ph.D. and Pharmacist licensure from ETH Zurich. He has served as a SPARK adviser since 2010.

Steven Schow, Ph.D., is the Vice President of Research and Development at Telik, Inc. He has over 35 years of pharmaceutical, biotech, and agrichemical industrial research and development experience. His work spans a wide range of indications, including psychotropic, anti-infective, cardiovascular, immunological, metabolic, and anticancer R&D, as well as research in novel insecticides. Dr. Schow has been a SPARK advisor and advocate since 2007.

Michael Taylor, Ph.D., DABT, is the Founder and Principal at Non-Clinical Safety Assessment, a consulting firm specializing in the development of drugs and medical devices. Dr. Taylor has more than 20 years of R&D experience in the pharmaceutical industry and has served on executive teams. He is a board-certified toxicologist and holds Ph.D. and M.S. degrees in Toxicology from Utah State University with postdoctoral training at the NIH and CNRS of France. He has been a SPARK advisor for the past 6 years.

Simeon Taylor received a Ph.D. in Biological Chemistry and an M.D.—both from Harvard University. He is a board-certified physician in the specialty of Internal Medicine and the subspecialty of Endocrinology & Metabolism. For the majority of his career, he worked in the Division of Intramural Research in the National Institute of Diabetes and Digestive and Kidney Disease, where he served as Chief of the Diabetes Branch (1989–2000). He has worked in the pharmaceutical industry since 2000, at Eli Lilly (2000–2002) and at Bristol-Myers Squibb (2002-present), where he currently serves as Vice President, Research & Scientific Affairs. During his time at Bristol-Myers Squibb, he led the Cardiovascular and Metabolic Disease Drug Discovery organization, which has advanced more than 25 compounds into development.

Stephen Venuto, Esq., focuses on the representation of high growth technology and media companies, their founders and investors. His practice includes the formation, financing, and general corporate counseling of emerging growth private and public companies; representation of venture capital firms and investment banks in private and public offerings; and other complex transactions. He is a member of the Emerging Companies Group at Orrick, Herrington & Sutcliffe LLP (Orrick).

Susan Wade has 25 years of industrial experience in the areas of Quality Assurance, Quality Control, and product development for manufacturers of pharmaceuticals and medical devices. She also has extensive experience with aseptic processing, sterile fill, and validation of products including API, proteins, antibodies, traditional pharmaceuticals, viral gene therapy vectors, autologous cell therapies, and orthopedic medical devices. She has global experience with audits, validation, analytical and bioanalytical assay development, as well as development of policies and systems for ISO, QSR, and GMP compliance.

John Walker is a biotechnology industry veteran with over 30 years of experience in the healthcare and biopharmaceutical industries. He received a B.A. in History from the State University of New York at Buffalo and is a graduate of the Advanced Executive Program, J. L. Kellogg Graduate School of Management at Northwestern University. Mr. Walker serves as chairman of the boards of directors of Renovis, KAI Pharmaceuticals, Guava Technologies, and Saegis Pharmaceuticals. He serves on the boards of directors for Geron and several privately held biotechnology companies. He also serves as an advisor to the SPARK Program at Stanford.